VOLUME
25

Originally published in the United Kingdom in weekly parts **COMBAT & SURVIVAL** is a study of the armed forces at work. It shows the skills taught to soldiers and the way in which military units operate. It examines the weapons and equipment used by different armies; and, by looking at recruit training and exercises, **COMBAT & SURVIVAL** demonstrates how the armed forces develop individual responsibility, leadership and initiative.

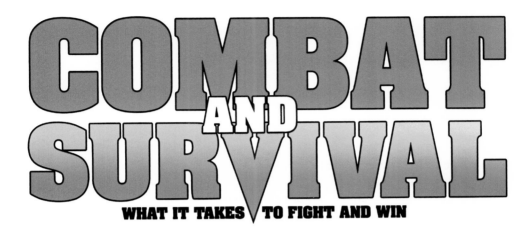

COMBAT AND SURVIVAL

WHAT IT TAKES TO FIGHT AND WIN

VOLUME
25

H. S. STUTTMAN, INC. *publishers*   Westport, Connecticut 06889

Contents

Volume 25

Published by H. S. STUTTMAN INC.
Westport, Connecticut 06889
© Aerospace Publishing 1991
ISBN 0-87475-560-3

SEARCHING FOR ARMS

As a soldier in Northern Ireland — or in any other internal security operation — you will need to become an expert in recognising and searching possible hiding places for terrorists' weapons, explosives and equipment. Terrorist organisations need these stores for their campaigns of terror. There are international suppliers who will sell weapons and explosives to terrorist organisations.

A proportion of these are intercepted by the security forces — such as the arms bound for the IRA that were found by the French authorities on board the *Eksund* in 1987 — but many more get through. These are smuggled into the country where the terrorists are operating and are hidden in ingenious places. Weapons or explosives can be stored under floorboards, up chimneys, behind false walls, in cellars or in attics. Farm outbuildings, haystacks, manure or silage heaps, sludge containers and buried oil-drums have all been used.

Illegal cargoes have been moved in false compartments in road tankers or other lorries. Single weapons or small amounts of ammunition have been moved in prams underneath babies,

Dog handlers in Xuan Loc province, South Vietnam, deploy their dogs on what could be an entrance to a VC bunker system. Dogs are invaluable in any search operation, although the terrorists can employ a number of countermeasures to reduce the effectiveness of the canine nose.

Factors for planning search operations

Before the operation, consider the following:
1 The area to be searched and the type of search.
2 The reason for the search.
3 Previous and ongoing friendly forces activity in the area.
4 All the available information on previous insurgent activity in the search area.
5 Who has given authority for the search?
6 How many search teams are you going to need for the job and how many are going to be available?
7 Cordon: you will need to cover any potential remote detonation firing points and sniper positions with cordon troops.
8 Time appreciation: how long is it all going to take, and what time constraints have you got?
9 When are you going to carry out the search: if you are not going to do it immediately, should you arrange for observation of the target in the meantime?

Identity card stamp
Pay particular attention to where the stamp crosses the edge of the photograph and the validity of the stamp itself.

Questions
When questioning a person about his identity documents, maintain eye contact and frame the questions as follows:
1 "What is your name?"
2 "Where do you live?"
3 "When were you born?"

Identity documents
In Vietnam many VC w[...] known as legal cadres, [...] having proper ID and li[...] quite openly as respec[...] members of village so[...] When checking ID, loo[...] carefully at the photog[...] Look at the individual a[...] to imagine him in the circumstances under w[...] the picture was taken [...] effective comparison.

Searching people
Unless the suspect produces an official pass exempting him from search, you must ask him or her to produce some form of identification and the frisk them. Pay attention to the armpits, stomach, the inside of the thighs and especially the groin, which inexperienced troops are loth to search properly and is a correspondingly popular area to hide things.

secreted in shopping bags or hidden on or even in the person. The number of potential hiding places is enormous.

Learn to look

The Royal Engineers provide expert search teams in Northern Ireland, but they cannot possibly cover the whole province, so each battalion sends soldiers, usually from the Assault Pioneer Platoon, to the School of Engineering at Chatham to attend a 'Search Techniques' course prior to a Northern Ireland tour.

Here they are taught search techniques in both urban and rural environments. They also learn how to disarm booby traps in case they are confronted with them while searching.

If your battalion is about to go on a tour of duty in Northern Ireland, and if you are interested in an especially challenging and interesting job while you are there, you would do well to volunteer for a 'search techniques' course.

Tell-tale signs

Searching in a rural environment largely involves having an eye for the ground. You can't thoroughly search large areas of countryside, but some common sense principles can yield

common sense principles can yield results out of all proportion to the number of people searching.

Put yourself in the mind of the individual hiding the weapons, ammunition or explosives. Normally, anyone hiding something in the country will choose a suitable marker such as a lone tree or a particularly prominent track junction. Often a search in the vicinity of such a 'marker' has produced results. The technique was perfected by a young Fusilier officer called Winthrop in the early 1970s and became known as the 'Winthrop method'.

Urban hiding places

In urban areas there are many more potential hiding places. But you can't search every house. It would cause such a storm of protest that it would be counter-productive in public relations terms; and to prevent material being smuggled out at one end of the estate while the other end was being searched, would require impossible numbers of soldiers to cordon and monitor the estate. Also, it would probably be more effective to use some or all of the soldiers in some other way.

Wait to be told

Searches in cities, therefore, are

normally undertaken only on receipt of specific intelligence. Then permission has to be sought (and is not always granted) from Brigade Headquarters before a search of a private house is sanctioned. Unless in 'hot pursuit' after a shooting incident, even a battalion commander may not authorise entry into, or search of, a private residence.

If, as a result of specific information, permission is granted for a search of a house, the householder will be

SEARCHING VILLAGES

The aim of counter-revolutionary operations is to destroy the revolutionary movement. But this does not just mean killing the insurgents: it must go hand-in-hand with political and social reform in order to remove the underlying causes for unrest.

Building construction techniques
You must have a thorough knowledge of how a type of building is constructed in order to know where the natural hiding places are: cavity walls, lofts, false ceilings etc.

Farm buildings
Farms will have underground drainage and manure pits that provide ready-built hiding places, and are by their nature difficult and unpleasant to search.

Clothing
Do not make the mistake of patting the clothing; it is very easy to miss flat objects such as thin laminated sheets of plastic explosive. Roll the cloth between your fingers, do not forget to check hats and have a good rummage around in long hair.

Snakes
The Viet Cong would sometimes use live snakes as booby traps in their tunnel systems by setting the snake in a bamboo tube in the roof and attaching a trip wire to the cap. Some species of snake are so deadly they were classified by the number of steps you can take after being bitten.

Booby trapping
Arms caches will not only be cleverly hidden but also booby-trapped. When you find something, do not touch it but call in the experts to check it out. Be careful where you site your incident checkpoint: if it is an obvious choice, you could sit on a command detonated device.

The tunnel rats
Searching bunker and tunnel system was an especially hazardous task, usually given to specialist search teams known as the Tunnel Rats. These tunnels, which could be the equivalent size of a small town, were heavily booby trapped. The best approach was to let the dog do the recce and then pump down quantities of tear gas before demolition. However, in some circumstances the tunnel rats would have to clear the system by hand, surviving on their wits, speed of reaction, and their Colt 45.

Phu Bai, Vietnam: a VC arms cache with a new AK-47 assault rifle still smeared in grease in the factory packing cases. Note the Chi Com chest webbing and spare magazines.

A soldier searches a likely spot for planting a landmine to take out the road above. Route clearance patrols of this type are vital if road movement is going to be secure.

informed that his house is going to be searched and he will be invited to accompany you during your search. If you have to cause damage – such as by lifting floorboards – the damage is always repaired immediately by special teams. The householder will be asked to sign a form stating that no damage has been caused or, if it has, that it has been or will be repaired.

Search equipment

As a member of a search team you are equipped and trained to do your job as quickly and efficiently as possible, and to cause as little damage as you can.

Apart from mundane items such as jemmies, spades and screwdrivers, you are equipped with metal detectors, explosives 'sniffers', inspection mirrors and fluorescent hand lamps. Most explosives 'sniffers' will indicate the presence of gelignite, dynamite, nitro-glycerine, nitro-benzine, DNT, TNT, RDX, PETN and other explosives. Equipment apart, you will probably have your greatest success by using your eyes and your common sense.

Major finds have been achieved by trained 'sniffer' dogs and their handlers. If you have a way with animals, this might be just the course for you. The handler and his dog work as an inseparable team, each trusting the other. Several types of dogs have been used but the most usual is the Labrador. It is an intelligent, strong and loyal animal that is prepared to work hard.

The range of search and detection equipment is enormous. There are various types of mirrors for looking underneath cars for explosive devices or booby-traps, and for looking in inaccessible corners. You can attach lights to them if there is insufficient light. There are various types of X-ray equipment. These may be the large machines permanently installed in airports, or portable versions for inspecting suspicious containers on site.

There are letter-bomb detectors that screen either individual letters and

A member of the special dog section listens out on the radio while the rest of the team are briefed on a search operation in support of joint RUC and Army operations in South Armagh.

packages or, in some cases, bundles of letters up to about 16 inches thick at a rate of about 9,000 an hour. They can detect virtually all known letter-bomb detonating devices.

There are any number of small hand-held metal detectors for frisking individuals and there are much more sophisticated explosives detectors that draw in air via the probe on the unit and analyse the sampled air for explosives vapour. If an explosive is detected the instrument will give off an alarm.

Complete package

Then there are complete search kits, which come in a container. These include light probes, extension rods, mirrors, recovery magnets, hooks, lock viewers and illuminated inspection mirrors. There are even endoscopes, which can be attached to still and video cameras to take photographs through small holes in packages, through keyholes or through observation holes in terrorist siege operations.

Flexible medical fibroscopes have been converted for use with radio-controlled remote operation, TV picture transmission and built-in illumination. They can be used to examine suspect containers or car boots for explosive devices from a safe distance.

On the spot

You may be able to search where the area has been secured and you are able to get on unmolested with your business. But often you may be in an altogether more dangerous situation, where you could be ambushed at any moment.

Everyone in the patrol will have his eyes skinned for something suspicious – for any mines, for movement

ARMS FIND

This rather mixed Irish National Liberation Army weapons find includes:

1 Assorted 12-bore shotgun ammo
2 Browning automatic shotgun
3 .303 ball ammunition
4 .303 Martini Henry rifle (unserviceable)
5 7.65-mm Astra pistol
6 9-mm MP 40 German sub-machine gun, of World War II vintage
7 Issue 2z 9-mm ball ammunition
8 Various .22 long rifle ammunition
9 .222 Remington rifle ammunition
10 7.65-mm pistol ammunition
11 MP 40 magazines

The weapons are a collection of wartime souvenirs and sporting firearms usually used by farmers, which indicate that these weapons were drawn from the community and not imported from overseas. The lack of a modern high-velocity rifle limits the value of the find, but the pistol and SMG would be useful for close-range work.

or for anything that has been disturbed or looks out of place. You may often have to clear a route.

A favourite terrorist tactic is to pack a road culvert with milk churns full of explosive and then to detonate it from a safe distance when a security forces, vehicle crosses the culvert. Obviously, foot patrols must look for these devices and the tell-tale signs that give them away if this sort of incident is going to be avoided. It will be up to you with your special training to identify likely sites for a bomb or for hidden weapons, explosives or ammunition.

Search training is a challenging business. It is not a skill for the faint-hearted or the lazy. You will be called out at all hours to search suspicious buildings or areas. You will need the guts to go in and search in dangerous circumstances. But, above all, you will need the native wit and intelligence to recognise a dodgy situation when you see one. Then it may be you who finds a hidden store of deadly Armalites or M60 machine-guns. If you do, you will deliver a body blow to the terrorists and save many lives.

A tunnel rat reaches out as a demolition charge is passed down to him for demolishing a main force VC tunnel complex north of An Khe. Note the .45 Colt for use in the extremely cramped conditions of the tunnels.

A demolition reveals a tunnel complex. The communication tunnels between rooms or sectors of a complex were nothing more than glorified rabbit holes just large enough for the average VC.

A tunnel rat ponders a tunnel entrance in Ho Bo woods north of Saigon. The tunnels were heavily booby-trapped and it took a special type of individual to fight in this environment.

Combat Report
Chad:
Counter-Insurgency Operations Part 1

A soldier based in Chad describes the guerrilla operations he was involved in, waging psychological warfare against the Libyan regular forces.

I had been in Chad for two months and most of the time had been spent becoming familiar with French weapons, brushing up on my fieldcraft and becoming acclimatised to the heat and flies. My Company consisted of all-British personnel who, like me, were on an 18 month renewable contract. Our job was to conduct a counter-insurgency operation against Libyan regular forces.

After moving up country, we conducted numerous guerilla operations hitting targets at random and quickly withdrawing, destroying supplies and generally harassing their positions and running before they could mount any counter-attack. We initially deprived the enemy of sleep and their morale and psychological condition was now at an all-time low. Occasionally, our two snipers would go forward and pick off any Officer or NCO who made a suitable target, thus depriving the men of leadership.

On one occasion, five men and I, under cover of darkness, went forward to harass an enemy position which was about five miles from our hides. The march to the objective was uneventful until we came to within about one mile of their position. Approximately 300 yards in front of us we could see clearly the silhouettes of an enemy patrol, consisting of about seven or eight men. We immediately went to ground, waiting for about 15 minutes to allow them to pass a safe distance from us. Then we continued to advance towards the objective. Now only a few hundred yards from the enemy positions, we lay in an extended line and examined the area through night sights.

We attacked in the dark

A paraflare was fired first, illuminating the position, and the Libyans could be seen looking frantically in all directions. By the time the flare was extinguished and the position was again blacked out, we had all noted our targets. Unlike conventional warfare where a position is bombarded whilst it is illuminated, we would obtain the psychological edge by attacking in the dark, using night sights. As soon as darkness fell once again, we opened up with heavy machine guns and mortars, firing HE and phosphorus, our snipers picking off any man who dared raise his head above the safety of the trench. We then quickly withdrew along a pre-arranged escape route, leaving the enemy nothing to launch a counter-attack against. Whilst tactically withdrawing, we would leave a visible trail for any pursuer to follow – we usually heard the explosion and the screams of men as they encountered our carefully placed, concealed booby traps.

After lying up for about two hours, we approached the position again – this time from an entirely different direction. The same tactics were used – as soon as they thought they were safe and could start to relax, they were fiercely attacked again, being kept pinned down in their trenches. This time, instead of completely withdrawing, we pulled back another 200 yards or so and waited for the patrol to come looking for us. Now in an ambush position, we could see the patrol carefully making its way towards us. The first person to open up was our Platoon Commander – immediately followed by the bark of machine gun fire and semi-automatic rifle fire. The patrol was engulfed in bright red tracer

rounds that resembled hundreds of luminous insects flying around in a frenzy. The enemy could only briefly fire back in our general direction: it was all over very quickly. Although we were small in number, we made up for this by being very heavily armed.

The bodies were searched and all personal papers that gave the soldiers' names, including letters from home, were read. Two men who spoke Arabic well, crawled as near to the enemy position as they could and began shouting out the dead men's names. Continuously changing position so that they could not be pin-pointed, they pretended to have been captured and cried out for help. They pretended they were being tortured and graphically described their ordeal. The occasional man would lift his head above a trench but would immediately become the target for a 7.62 round fired by one of our snipers. For several hours the enemy heard blood curdling screams and pathetic cries for help. Then the tactics were changed. In Arabic,

Heavily outnumbered, our best bet was to harass the enemy to keep them off-balance. With sniper and mortar attacks we inflicted numerous casualties on them after the main attack.

the enemy heard warnings "they have broken into our position", "they're killing us at random". Again, the snipers would take out anyone who moved.

We withdrew, after dragging the bodies as close to the enemy position as we could while the snipers kept the enemy heads down to mask our activities. This was pure psychological warfare or, as we called it, 'scare the **** out of them time'.

The main body of us withdrew, leaving two men concealed in a position overlooking the enemy. We later learnt that we had dragged the dead men dangerously close to the enemy and if our snipers had not done such a good job we would have been clearly visible from the gun trench. The men manning the observation post later reported that panic broke out when the bodies were found and intercepted enemy radio messages were found to have exaggerated our activities even more. Harassing techniques were carried out for another three days – at night the enemy was pounded with automatic fire and mortars and, during the day, snipers would pick targets at random, continuously moving to avoid detection – bang one, then move.

WORKING WITH I.S. VEHICLES

At the start of the present troubles in Northern Ireland the Army had no specialist riot control vehicles and had to adapt existing vehicles for the job. This Land Rover is unprotected except for the hasty addition of a neck wire-cutting bar welded to the side of the vehicle to protect against wires stretched across the roads.

Most armoured personnel carriers (APCs) are tracked, for top cross-country performance — but a tracked vehicle is not best suited for internal security work. They are often difficult and expensive to operate; they damage road surfaces; their design is often too complex for the needs of IS – but, most important of all, laymen and the media think of them as 'tanks'.

How often have you heard on TV about 'tanks' intervening on the streets in some foreign country? Usually, the vehicles are actually tracked APCs. In a Western democracy, the use of 'tanks' in IS is politically unacceptable. Besides, most IS vehicles operate on roads and in towns. So purpose-built IS vehicles are now used throughout the world.

The ideal IS vehicle

Most are 4×4 wheeled vehicles, armoured against small-arms fire up to and including 7.62-mm, although some heavier IS vehicles are proof against 7.62-mm armour-piercing rounds.

IS vehicles need observation blocks, so that you can see what is happening around you. In a conventional battle, with the vehicle operating in a wide open space along with many others and with infantry on the ground, it is not so vital that all members of the crew have a comprehensive view of the ground. But, in a city street, to stop a petrol bomber approaching an armoured vehicle via a blind spot, the ideal IS vehicle must have all-round vision. Observation blocks and firing ports allow you to

use your weapon from within the vehicle.

Vulnerable points on the vehicle – such as the fuel tank and the radiator – need special protection, particularly from petrol bombs. The other main threat is from anti-tank grenades. In Northern Ireland, the IRA has used RPG-7 rocket launchers against IS vehicles with limited success. IS vehicles don't have enough armour to stop rockets. But urban terrorists have to engage IS vehicles at close range. This means that the firer has very little time to recognise the target, prepare to fire, acquire the target, aim and fire. Often RPG-7 projectiles have passed behind their target, on some occasions unnoticed by the occupants.

One way round the problem is to fix a steel mesh sheet on either side of the

The Hippo is one of the older anti-mine vehicles developed by the South African Defence Force that has been widely used in the townships for riot control. The 'V'-shaped double hull gives good protection against conventional anti-tank mines.

vehicle, half a metre or so proud of the side, so that any warhead is detonated prematurely and loses its penetrative power against the armour.

The ideal IS vehicle hull is designed so that, if one of the wheels triggers a land mine, the upward slope of the hull will deflect most of the blast. A strong monocoque structure will provide maximum protection, so long as you and the rest of the crew are strapped in your seats. The South

RIOT CONTROL VEHICLES

Internal Security vehicles have to be able to fulfil a number of operational roles, from police actions through to paramilitary and counter-terrorist functions. Design is always likely to be a compromise between roles, and unfortunately design of the vehicles can severely limit tactical options.

Communications
Command and control in an urban area is difficult at the best of times. In a riot, effective passage of information becomes all-important. You must have bomb-proof communications between vehicles and from outside the vehicle to those on the ground.

The Buffel
The Buffel troop carrier offers almost total protection from landmines, as well as small-arms fire. It gives good protection as a troop carrier, but is far from ideal in a riot situation as it is open-topped: the crew are vulnerable to missiles and petrol bombs.

African Ingwe vehicle, the British GKN Sankey Saxon and Italy's Fiat 6614CM APC all have shaped hulls.

Entrance and exit

An IS vehicle must let you and the rest of your section get in and out quickly. It's wise to have more than one door. In a conventional war, the enemy is usually expected from a single direction. When your vehicle stops, it will be pointing at the enemy and your objective. But guerrillas may attack you from any direction, and you need to be able to keep the vehicle between you and the enemy.

An IS vehicle will therefore normally have single side doors and double back doors. Side doors also mean having a vehicle with only four wheels, which also makes for simplicity and mechanical reliability.

IS vehicles should be simple and rugged, since they will often be used in countries with limited maintenance resources. The Saxon is powered by the widely-available Bedford 500 6-cylinder diesel truck engine, so that anyone who can maintain a truck can also maintain the Saxon. You could well find yourself inside a Saxon, as several UK-based British battalions are equipped with them.

Small design details are also very important. For example, in the Belgian Beherman Demoen BDX, the engine air intake is below the generous canopy over the driving position and has a moving shutter to protect

The Buffel is the most recent addition to the South African internal security vehicle fleet. Again, it is mine- and small-arms fire-resistant.

Weapon mounts
Good IS vehicles should be capable of mounting a wide range of weapon systems so they can be quickly refitted to cope with a changing threat, from water cannon CS gas and smoke dispensers to 20-mm cannon.

Debussing
There must be exits on three sides of the vehicle, and the doors must open to cover debussing troops.

rricades
vehicles should be robust ough to demolish most tily-erected vehicle ricades without damage d at speed.

Fire
The vehicle must not be vulnerable to petrol bombs or other incendiary devices. Vehicle system must be protected from fire damage, as must the crew, and some sort of automatic fire suppression system is a must. Both the Buffel and Casspir are vulnerable to petrol bomb attack.

Protection
IS vehicles should at the very least give protection from stones and other hand-thrown missiles and petrol bombs. At the other end of the scale, some IS vehicles have more in common with a tank than a police car, giving protection from mine blast, small-arms fire and even rocket-propelled grenades.

The Casspir
This vehicle is widely used by the South African police and military as an internal security vehicle, usually for operations against terrorist units in the bush rather than as a riot control vehicle.

All-round vision
In order to control a situation you must have protected 360-degree vision. An IS vehicle with blind spots is a recipe for disaster: rioters soon learn of any weaknesses of design.

Firing ports
Firing ports allow riot control agents, baton rounds or small arms to be fired from the relative safety of inside the vehicle. The Casspir has an open top as well as firing ports and windows so that the crew can also fire over the side of the vehicle. This offers a better field of view and fire, but obviously less protection.

Wheels or tracks
Wheeled vehicles are generally faster and more manoeuvrable than tracked vehicles. In most countries, the use of tracked vehicles for internal security is politically unacceptable.

Crew comfort
Internal security duty usually involves protracted periods waiting for something to happen. An uncomfortable, cramped vehicle will reduce crew efficiency by increasing crew and passenger fatigue.

1453

injure the occupants of open vehicles.

Water cannon vehicles may or may not be armoured; conventional 'soft skin' vehicles can be covered in a form of appliqué lightweight armour against blast and low velocity rounds.

Appliqué armour was first developed for the British Army to protect Land Rover crews against blast, fire and acid bombs, and low-velocity small arms fire. GRP is a form of glass-fibre used to cover the body and roof of Land Rovers, while Macralon, a form of strengthened plastic, is used to cover the windscreen and windows. If you serve in Northern Ireland you will travel in 'Pigs' and armoured Land Rovers.

against Molotov cocktails. The twin exhaust pipes run along the sides of the roof to make it more difficult to climb onto the vehicle.

Weapons, equipment and armour

IS vehicles can be fitted with a variety of armaments, including water cannon, tear-gas launchers and machine-guns. Some can even be electrified to prevent rioters climbing onto them.

Many other ingenious devices have been developed. In Northern Ireland, for example, the British Army has adapted the long-serving GKN Sankey AT-104 IS vehicle, commonly known as the 'Pig', by attaching unfolding fenders to each side of the vehicle. So,

A Saracan armoured car wrecked by a massive culvert bomb. IS vehicles must be optimised for maximum crew protection from this type of attack. The Saracen was not primarily designed to cope with this threat.

if you park the vehicle in the middle of a relatively narrow road flanked by buildings, you can block most of the road off and be protected from missiles thrown by rioters. This adaptation is known as the 'Flying Pig'.

Other possible equipment includes roof- or turret-mounted searchlights, loudspeaker systems and a 'cow-catcher' device for removing barricades. Many jeeps and Land Rovers on IS work have a fence picket attached vertically to the front, to cut steel wires stretched across roads to

Discretion and disguise

The other sort of IS vehicle that you could come across is the so-called Discreet Operational Vehicle, or DOV. A growing number of police forces throughout the world are recognising that DOVs – standard commercial vehicles and limousines that are armoured without appearing to be so – are less provocative than the more heavily armoured, obviously military hybrid vehicles.

If you are in the middle of a riot, or patrolling an area in which you are highly likely to get shot at, you would be better off in a highly protected conventional armoured vehicle. But in some situations DOVs are more suitable and just as effective – when dealing with lightly armed terrorists, student demonstrations and the transport of government VIPs, for example.

No DOV can be completely bullet proof. The best protection can only buy time. The armoured Lincoln Continental delivered to the US Secret Service in 1969 carried two tons of armour and bullet-resistant glass and

Above: The Transaif multi-role armoured vehicle is very nearly the last word in riot control vehicles. The vehicles offers full protection from small-arms fire and fragmentation in a range of models so that the same vehicle can be used for a variety of IS tasks.

Right: The Transaif can carry 14 fully-equipped personnel, protected from a hostile environment whilst maintaining a non-aggressive profile. It has three exits and can be used off-road. The tyres are bullet-resistant run-flat type and there is an inbuilt fire suppression system.

Above: The Berliet VXB 170 is currently in service with the French Gendarmerie, who are equipped with a wide range of armoured vehicles.

Right: This Humber armoured car or 'Pig' fitted with armoured screens which fold flat against the side of the vehicle and are swung out to provide protection from missiles. This excellent modification is known as a 'Flying Pig'.

Shorts of Belfast produced several different Shorland armoured Land Rover designs. This model had a well-protected crew compartment but no skirts, so explosives could be rolled underneath it and the vehicle knocked out. Note the smoke dischargers fitted to the turret.

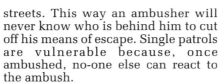

The Commando Police Emergency Rescue Vehicle manufactured by Cadillac Gage has six vision blocks, eight gun ports and provision for mounting forward of the top hatch a 7.62-mm or 12.7-mm machine-gun. The ERV has a three-man crew.

The Saracen, although proof against small-arms fire, is vulnerable – as are all armoured vehicles – to hand-held anti-tank weapons such as the RPG-7. This vehicle is fitted with wire mesh to prematurely detonate the HEAT warhead from an RPG.

was capable of travelling at 50 mph with all the tyres shot out.

The Secret Service would be the first to admit that its most attractive characteristic was its ability to keep going with all its tyres deflated – even that mass of armour could not protect the occupants from sustained fire from high-powered automatic rifles. It might have resisted the first few rounds, giving time for agents travelling in back-up vehicles to return fire, or for the chauffeur in the protected limousine to put his foot on the accelerator.

Tactics

Although you may see police DOVs, you are unlikely to work with them yourself. It is the 'Pigs', armoured Land Rovers, Saxons and armoured bulldozers that you will learn to work with. Much of your patrolling in IS work will be done in a vehicle. It means more ground can be covered more quickly.

The way that you can avoid ambush is to work in multiple patrols – in other words, several vehicles working simultaneously in parallel or nearby

streets. This way an ambusher will never know who is behind him to cut off his means of escape. Single patrols are vulnerable because, once ambushed, no-one else can react to the ambush.

Working inside cramped armoured vehicles, particularly in hot weather, is not pleasant. But the armour around you may well save your life. The IS

vehicle gives a high degree of protection and security to you and your mates. It is one more weapon in the fight against terrorism.

This RUC armoured Land Rover was hit by an RPG round, killing one and seriously injuring another police officer. Riot control vehicles must be designed to counter a wide range of threats, and some compromises have to be made.

Combat Report

Chad:
Counter-Insurgency Operations Part 2

Further events in Chad, with the guerrillas engaging the Libyan regular forces.

One evening we were informed that our Section was to act as pathfinders for a larger force that was to assault the position. The plan was for us to immobilise the enemy defences (consisting mainly of trip flares) and then, along with the main force, fight our way through the lines. This would take place after the position had been bombarded by heavy mortars.

The bombardment was impressive. By the light of paraflares, a spotter controlled the fire by radio and, in no time at all, the fire was becoming frighteningly accurate. I saw at least two trenches receive direct hits and, on a number of occasions as the rounds came closer, some of the enemy began to panic and run to other trenches only to be immediately hit by the red hot shrapnel.

Twice I dropped the split pin

The bombardment suddenly ceased and the area was again plunged into darkness. My Section crawled forward as our objective was to secure the trip flares with pins so the assault force could move forward unhindered. Although this may sound quite easy, the main problem was that we were aware the flares were within the arc of fire of a heavy machine gun and several other trenches. If we were detected or we accidentally set off a flare, there would be no way that we would be able to survive the immense fire that would be directed at us. We were lightly equipped in only belt order and submachine guns as we could not afford anything snagging on the trip wires and, if we

Supplied by the French to the Chadian forces, both sides ended up using Thomson-Brandt 120-mm mortars like this one.

had to move in a hurry, we would need every advantage on our side, with no excess weight to slow us down.

The securing of the flares could have only taken a few minutes but it seemed like a lifetime. The thought of the machine gun preyed continuously on my mind and I prayed that I did not set the flare off. Twice I dropped the split pin as I attempted, nervously, to push it through its securing hole. When, finally I secured the flare, I checked and double checked that it would not ignite. We now beckoned on the rest of the assault group who immediately crawled forward as our snipers kept the trenches occupied. We were now alarmingly close to the trenches and, as we crawled very slowly and cautiously, I heard the pinging noise that I knew a trip flare makes prior to igniting. It was such as familiar noise that everyone turned and looked in the direction of the sound. One of our men had become entangled in a previously unnoticed trip wire, the intense light now making him visible from every position.

The enemy, who up to now had been suffering heavy casualties and mental torment from opponents who they had never seen, now took their revenge. As every position opened up on the lone figure outlined against the night sky, he was killed instantly. We could do nothing but watch in sick horror as, even after he was so obviously dead, the fire continued – round after round of machine gun fire hitting him, causing his body to bounce across the ground. Added to our horror was the realisation that it would only be a matter of time before we, too, were detected.

Our entire assault team rose to their feet and skirmished forward. Weapons of all types opened up as men fell on all sides: some dying instantly, others screaming in mortal agony. Still onwards we pressed, taking no notice of what

was happening around us. I suddenly came across a trench and looked down at two startled Libyans who were manning a heavy machine gun. I gave a quick burst from my SMG, hitting them both, and moved towards another trench. By this time, there was chaos all around me: men running in all directions; the sound of intense gun fire; the choking smell of smoke and the almost unbearable screams of the wounded.

At times it was difficult to differentiate between friend and foe. As well as close quarter fire fights, there was also hand to hand combat, with men fighting in trenches and locked in battle, rolling around the ground. Out of the corner of my eye, I saw a Libyan officer running towards me with an AKM in his hands. I had no time to aim, I just fired a burst from the hip and shot him in the stomach. Some say this is the most painful area of the body in which to be shot. He sunk to the ground while clutching his abdomen and a startled look passed across his face as he stared at me. I suddenly realised that he thought I was one of his own men. As I watched him, something hit me across the head and I naturally assumed I had been hit by a bullet. I fell, dazed, into a trench and landed on top of two Libyans. I had been felled by a rifle butt. At first the soldiers ignored me, obviously thinking I was dead, but one must have seen me move and he lunged at me with a fixed bayonet on his rifle. Fortunately, I was able to avoid the blow, the bayonet and barrel of the rifle digging deep but harmlessly into the side of the trench.

I had lost my weapon and the only form of defence left to me was my personal, highly sharpened bayonet that I had had since I was in the Parachute Regiment. Quickly, I pulled the bayonet from its metal scabbard, grabbed the soldier by his jaw and cut through the carotid artery. As the blood gushed like a fountain and the dead soldier crashed to the ground, I was grabbed from behind by the remaining soldier, his hands around my neck.

I broke his grip

I felt the strength draining from me and my heart was pounding. Fortunately for me, the unarmed combat I had been taught whilst in the Paras flashed through my mind. Violently twisting my body, I broke his grip on my throat. After turning to face him, I jabbed at his left eye with my bent thumb and immediately followed up with a punch to the throat. As he fell to his knees, I sat astride him, holding him by the jaw and back of the head and twisted his neck with one fast, violent jerk. Tired, I sat down in the trench to rest for a while and get my thoughts together.

The sounds of battle still echoed around me and the light of the paraflares twinkled on the faces of the two men I had just killed, one his face pale due to loss of blood and the other with his head bent at a strange and distorted angle. At that moment, instead of feeling remorse, I silently thanked the little Jamaican instructor from the Parachute Regiment who had taught me to fight like a cornered animal. After searching the bottom of the trench with my hands, I found the bayonet that I had had for many years but which had only been christened this day.

As I laboriously clambered out of the trench, I saw one of our men, knife in hand, squaring up. The soldier, startled by my presence, spun around in my direction but immediately relaxed as he recognised me. The battle was finally over.

BOMB DISPOSAL

A favourite terrorist weapon is the bomb – whether used against military targets, against business centres like shops and factories or, as often as not, against any convenient target to disrupt everyday life as thoroughly as possible.

The reason why terrorists would attack military targets is clear enough. Attacks on economic targets are part of a long-term strategy and are designed to undermine the ability and determination of the legitimate government to carry on the war against terrorism. Clearly, the more expensive a campaign becomes, the more difficult it is to justify to the taxpayer in a democratic state. This is why the IRA has regularly bombed factories, shops and other economic targets in Northern Ireland.

Indiscriminate bombing is, perhaps, terrorism in its purest form.

ACTION ON FINDING AN IMPROVISED EXPLOSIVE DEVICE

1. Confirm
Check that there is a threat, i.e. that it may well be a bomb; and that you know what it looks like and exactly where it is.

2. Clear
Report the object immediately and move all the inhabitants in the vicinity of the device to a safe area.

3. Cordon
When the area is clear, cordon troops must guard the area to ensure that no-one enters the danger area. White mine tape should be put out and all barriers and potential entry points should be manned.

4. Control
Appoint a cordon commander to control all movement and help collect keys from locals to buildings in the danger area that may be locked. Set up an incident control point well outside the danger area to co-ordinate further action.

The results of a large car bomb detonated in Tu Do street in Saigon. VC sapper units in Saigon played a significant part in the Tet offensive and caused damage to American morale out of all proportion to their number or the actual physical threat they represented.

Combat Skills

COMMAND DETONATION

Terrorists can use a variety of means to detonate bombs and land mines. Timer rundown is perhaps the most common for attacking static targets, but for moving targets such as a vehicle convoy the terrorist must be able to observe the convoy to fire the mine, either electrically by command wire or by frequency induction, i.e. radio control. The best defence against this type of attack is to physically clear with foot patrols all likely firing points that overlook the convoy route. Aggressive patrolling will also prevent or discourage terrorists from placing landmines. Mines and culvert bombs can also be set to detonate by vehicle influence such as vibration, audio frequency of the engine or magnetic influence.

The only way to prevent this type of attack is to get out on the ground and dominate the area with patrols, covert and overt OPs, planting unmanned ground sensors and air photography.

Above: These are the twisted remains of an armoured Land Rover carrying members of the Parachute Regiment on an open stretch of dual carriageway towards Warren Point, Northern Ireland.

Above: The first bomb detonated in the Warren Point attack was hidden in bales of hay on a trailer parked on the side of the road. The four-tonner took the full force of the blast as it drove past.

This massive crater is all that remains of the stone gatehouse chosen as the Incident Control Point. The IRA correctly anticipated its use and mined it.

Creating a constant atmosphere of terror is intended to so terrify and intimidate the population that they will be cowed into submission. Aircraft, shopping precincts, hotel lobbies and airport check-in facilities are but a few of the many public places that have been bombed by the Red Army Faction, the Baader-Meinhof Group, Palestinian terrorists, Sikh extremists, the IRA and many other terrorist groups in recent years.

Delivering the goods

Terrorist explosive devices vary according to the nature of the target and the skill of the bomber. They may incorporate commercial or home-made explosives and be initiated by command detonation or a timing device, or be set off by the target.

Perhaps the commonest method of transporting and placing a bomb is by using a car. The so-called 'car-bomb' has become almost commonplace as a method of terrorist attack across the world. In the Lebanon in 1983-4 a huge cargo of explosive was packed into lorries and driven by suicidal Palestinians straight at buildings occupied by US and French troops of the four-power peacekeeping forces. The method proved horrifyingly effective: in a single attack, 241 US marines were crushed to death in their collapsed barrack block.

A variation of the 'car-bomb' is the so-called 'proxy' bomb, a technique developed by the IRA in Northern Ireland. The terrorists intimidate an individual (usually by holding his family hostage under threat of death) to drive a 'car-bomb' to a target and leave it there. 'Proxy' bombs are normally activated by means of a timing mechanism.

Bomb-making equipment is cleverly hidden in a lift-out section of floor in derelict housing in West Belfast. Finds of this type could be booby-trapped, and removal is left to specialists.

Left: In addition to dogs, electronic explosive sniffers have been deployed and are a useful deterrent to potential car bombers who run the gauntlet of VCPs equipped with these sniffers.

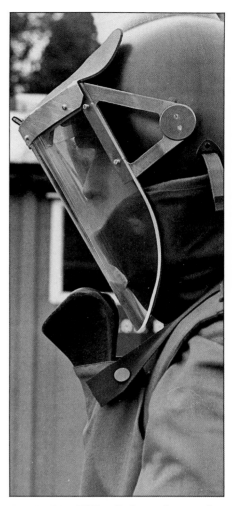

Sometimes you'll be warned of a bomb attack by telephone, which allows you to evacuate innocent civilians from the vicinity. This technique causes maximum disruption and damage, while at the same time giving the impression that it is not the terrorists' wish to harm anyone.

Triggering the blast

The command wire improvised explosive device (CWIED) and radio controlled improvised explosive device (RCIED) are the most difficult types of bombs to guard against. The first requires the individual initiating the bomb to be at the end of a wire where he can see the target. The second provides the bomber with greater flexibility, but it also calls for more sophisticated equipment. Much research is going on into ways of countering RCIEDs. The third main means of setting off a bomb is by 'target influence', whereby the presence of the target initiates a trembler or similar device. The best defence against these threats for you are vigilance, good tactics and accurate intelligence.

An ammunition technical officer is helped into his EOD suit prior to tackling a suspect device in Londonderry city centre, where a controlled explosion of the device may not be an option.

Another method of delivering high explosive to a target – one much favoured by the IRA – is the home-made mortar. Guerrilla movements all over the world have used mortars, but have usually been able to acquire properly manufactured weapons, either from the international arms market or by acquiring them in action from government troops.

In Northern Ireland it has so far proved too difficult for the IRA to smuggle such bulky weapons into the country. In any case, their sophisticated sighting systems make them unnecessarily complicated for the IRA's simple requirement – to lob high explosive a short distance into a security force base. Instead, they have developed a series of ingenious home-made mortars, which – although unreliable and unpredictable – have sometimes managed to inflict casualties inside security force bases.

What to look for

You will be watching for three kinds of terrorist bombs. Some consist of hundreds of pounds of explosives and

Bomb blankets made of layers of Kevlar will considerably reduce the fragmentation and blast effect of bombs. Kevlar envelopes are also available for transporting letter bombs to a safe area for destruction.

Detail of the EOD suit shows the massive steel shaped blastplate that protects the neck and chest. Note how it is shaped to direct the blast around the neck. The only unprotected area is the hands.

Dog teams are essential for search operations as the canine nose is perhaps the most sensitive explosive-sniffer around.

Combat Skills

Car bombs are often fitted with comprehensive anti-handling devices, so gaining entry to the car can be a very risky business. EOD have modified the 84-mm MAW for remote control firing for gaining entry to car bombs.

The effect of the 84-mm EOD round. The bomb disposal officer's task is made a good deal easier, and if the bomb does not go off when the round is fired it may well do enough damage to the initiation circuit to render it inoperative.

can be secreted in a vehicle or a large container. Others, used against individual targets, are altogether smaller and often more sophisticated affairs, which can be attached to the underside of a car, to a door or even delivered by post. The third category of bomb is the incendiary. This is an even smaller device that can be placed easily under inflammable materials in a warehouse or shop with a small timing device attached to it. The device bursts into flame for long enough to start a fire in the target building.

Bomb detection and disposal have developed rapidly since the early 1970s. The British Army, like other major armies of the world, already had bomb disposal experts before the present 'troubles' in Northern Ireland. These soldiers were mostly employed

Below: Remote control robots such as 'Wheelbarrow' greatly reduce the risk involved in dealing with IEDs. They are equipped with cameras, explosive sniffers, probes and a shotgun.

in dealing with unexploded German bombs left over from World War II. The Royal Engineers deals with unexploded bombs on the battlefield. The Royal Air Force deals with bombs on its own airfields, and the Royal Navy with mines in the sea and on the beaches.

But the dangerous task of dealing

with improvised explosive devices (IEDs) has always been the responsibility of the ammunition technical officers (ATOs) of the Royal Army Ordnance Corps (RAOC). Before working in Northern Ireland they had been dealing with IEDs in Aden, Cyprus, Hong Kong, Malaysia and other 'colonial' trouble spots.

Above: Earlier searching devices have now been overtaken by issue pieces of kit such as this telescoping rod, torch and mirror.

Body searching is extremely time-consuming, and in many situations there is insufficient manpower to check everyone. With this hand-held metal detector security personnel can quickly check everyone of either sex.

The hands-off approach

The best way for an ATO to disarm an IED is by using his hands and his expertise. But it is often suicidal to approach an IED; so a method of dealing with these devices was developed, using remote-controlled robot vehicles. These allow the ATO to remain at a safe distance while he locates, identifies and monitors a suspected bomb. If he decides that the object is too dangerous to be approached, he can attempt to disarm or destroy it by using various aids on the vehicle.

One of the best known of these vehicles is Wheelbarrow. It has a TV camera and monitor to allow remote surveillance, lights to illuminate the target, a shotgun to break car windows and a disrupter to render the firing mechanism of an explosive device harmless. Over the years, Wheelbarrow and other systems like it have saved many bomb disposal experts' lives.

If a personal approach to a bomb is unavoidable, the ATO will wear an explosive ordnance disposal (EOD) suit, which is designed to give some protection against fragments, blast and flames. He will carry an inspection set including probes, extension rods, mirrors, magnets, endoscopes, stethoscopes and simple hook and line devices. All of these will help him to inspect and deal with the IED. It is a delicate and dangerous task. The bravery of these men is quite exceptional.

Bombs and you

An ATO cannot operate alone. He may have to disarm a device in open countryside where he risks being shot at. Or the bomb may be in an urban area where there are hostile crowds. The ATO, his team and his equipment will have to be protected. This is where you come in.

Wheelbarrow in action. Although developed with internal security in mind, the system and its successors have been used extensively in the Falklands in mine-clearing operations.

The area may well have to be sealed off, both to protect the ATO and to prevent injury to innocent civilians. Sometimes terrorists will telephone a warning that they have left a bomb at a particular place, where it is due to explode at a certain time. This may give you time to go in, evacuate the area, perhaps help old and infirm people who are otherwise unable to move, and then guard the area to prevent anyone else going back into it. This may take a lot of soldiers.

If you are relatively close to the bomb, make sure that you have some cover between you and it. Then you don't get hit by debris if and when it does go off.

The threat from terrorist bombs is something we have had to live with since the early 1970s. It is a worldwide problem, which can be understood best if one realises that, in one month alone in 1976 in the United States, there were 763 bomb incidents. They caused 28 deaths, 132 injuries and damage costing $7 million. The threat continues today. We owe much to the courageous men who risk their lives by tackling these bombs. You can help by making the environment in which they have to work more secure.

The effect of a 500-lb culvert bomb. Although terrorists have limited supplies of quality commercial or military explosives, they have shown themselves very adept at using tertiary explosives made up of agricultural fertilisers and diesel etc.

NBC Survival Drills No. 6
CHECKS BEFORE TREATING A CASUALTY
FOLLOW THIS PROCEDURE

Chemical casualties are horrific and shocking, and most will at first seem to be beyond help — but many will recover as long as they get the right first aid in time. Each group of chemicals – nerve, blister, choking or blood agents – produces its own distinct symptoms. Each calls for a specific first aid treatment, so learn to recognise the symptoms at once. If you give the wrong treatment you could, at worst, kill the casualty, and at best you'll make his suffering worse.

**YOU ARE
NOT MASKED**

**YOU ARE
MASKED**

YOU FIND A CASUALTY

**NEAR YOUR
POSITION**

**SOME WAY FROM
YOUR POSITION**

**DID YOU UNMASK
AFTER THE ATTACK?**

**MASK UP (CHEMICAL
IMMEDIATE
ACTION DRILL)**

Use your common sense

Your first priority is to avoid becoming a casualty yourself. When you're treating someone else, therefore, make sure you are fully protected. There are occasions when you won't need to mask up, however. If you come across a casualty who's definitely a blood agent victim when you yourself have already unmasked, there's no need to mask up again or to mask the victim. The agent will have dispersed and can't harm you, while the casualty needs all the help he can get to breathe.

So, use your common sense. There simply aren't any hard and fast rules that apply to every kind of chemical injury.

YES   **NO**

**IF THE CASUALTY
IS MASKED,
UNMASK HIM**

**IF THE CASUALTY IS UNMASKED,
MASK HIM**

If you unmasked after the attack and are still breathing then you can obviously unmask the casualty, which will help him to breathe.

You are masked, and found the casualty some way from your position. If he is unmasked, put his respirator on for him.

DO YOU KNOW WHAT AGENT WAS USED ?

**NERVE
CHOKING
BLOOD
BLISTER**

YES

NO

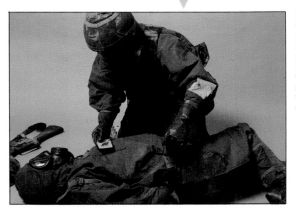

If you don't know whether the casualty has been injured by nerve, choking, blood or blister agent, wipe him and the surrounding area with three-colour detector paper.

YES — **RESULT** ? — **NO**

TREAT HIM
If you are sure that the casualty is a victim of nerve agent poisoning, treat him with his own Combopen and leave the empty syringe with him to tell medical staff he has already been injected.

Carefully examine his symptoms to determine which agent has poisoned him and give the appropriate treatment.

Classification of chemical agents

In order to treat chemical casualties you must be familiar with the main types of agent in the Warsaw Pact armoury and what symptoms they produce. There are three types of classification:

1 Military use
2 Duration and effectiveness
3 Effects on the body

1 Military use

This classifies the agents according to their primary tactical use in war.

a) Lethal agents
The aim of these agents is to inflict maximum fatalities.
b) Damaging agents
These are designed to cause either transitory or permanent damage to unprotected personnel. They may also cause death.
c) Incapacitating agents
These will not kill or permanently damage, but will incapacitate.

2 Effectiveness and duration

Basically, all agents can be divided into two categories: those that are persistent and those that quickly disperse after use, i.e. non-persistent.

a) Non-persistent
These are usually gases or liquids which disperse very rapidly, although they may produce a short-term downwind hazard.
b) Persistent
These are solids or liquids which disperse very slowly and provide a contact and vapour hazard for some considerable time in the target area.

3 Effects on the body

The third and most important classification as far as treating chemical agents is concerned is the effect they have on the casualty. You must be completely familiar with the types of agent in this classification if you are going to have any chance of correct diagnosis.

a) Nerve agents
These interfere with the motor nerve reflex arc in the brain and thus disrupt essential body functions, causing death very quickly when present in minute quantities.
b) Blood agents
These prevent your body from absorbing oxygen into your bloodstream, which in turn starves the tissues of oxygen and causes death.
c) Choking agents
These agents attack and damage the breathing passages and lungs, causing the damaged tissue to produce quantities of fluid in the lungs in which you drown.
d) Blister agents
These cause blistering and superficial destruction of any tissue they come into contact with. They can be fatal, but are usually classified as a damaging agent.
e) Physical and mental incapacitants
These temporarily disable by their effect on the brain or the body. While they are usually not permanently damaging, some, like LSD, can prove fatal and have long-term effects.

WHICH POISON?

PUPILS PINPOINTED

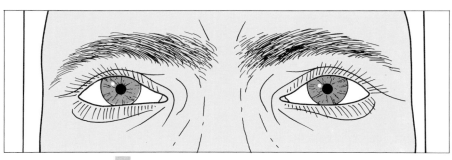

In most cases you will not know what agent has been used. You must work this out from the symptoms and signs of chemical poisoning in the casualty. He or she is going to be in a highly distressed state, but you must do this calmly, quickly and, most important, logically. When you are sure of the agent type give the first aid specific to that type of poisoning.

ARE THERE SIGNS OF NERVE AGENT POISONING?

If the casualty has pinpointed pupils, look for running eyes and nose, muscular twitching, stomach pain and difficulty in breathing. If some or all of these symptoms are present, treat for nerve agent poisoning.

Where to start

First, look at the casualty's eyes: they will give the best clue and tell you what other symptoms to look for to confirm which agent has been used.

There are three different eye conditions that narrow down the possibilities:

1 Pupils pinpointed
2 Pupils dilated (large)
3 Pupils normal

This gives you three starting points. Use the three diagrams to help you decide which agent has been used.

TREAT FOR NERVE AGENT POISONING

YES   **NO**

UNKNOWN AGENT: EVACUATE CASUALTY TO MEDICAL AID

As soon as you have satisfied yourself there is sufficient evidence of nerve agent poisoning, use the Combopen. If you hesitate, he may die.

If there are no symptoms of nerve agent poisoning, do not use the Combopen: you will simply add atropine poisoning to the casualty's problems. You will be dealing with an unknown agent, so evacuate the casualty as soon as possible.

PUPILS DILATED

HAS THE CASUALTY USED SOME OR ALL OF HIS COMBOPENS?

Pupils dilated usually means atropine poisoning. Check his respirator pouch to see how many Combopens have been used.

YES   **NO**   **CHECK FOR MENTAL INCAPACITANTS**

If all his Combopens are still there unused, look for the following: a confused mental state, inability to balance, a high pulse rate, and dry skin. If some or all of these symptoms are present, treat the casualty for poisoning by mental incapacitants.

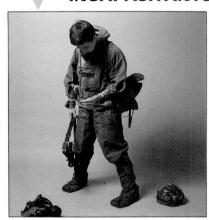

If there is no unsteadiness on the feet or confusion, look for a very dry mouth, hot dry skin and a high pulse rate. If some or all of these symptoms are present, assume the casualty is suffering from atropine poisoning.

YES NO

D YES

TREAT FOR ATROPINE POISONING	TREAT FOR MENTAL INCAPACI- TANT

UNKNOWN AGENT: EVACUATE CASUALTY TO MEDICAL AID

PUPILS NORMAL

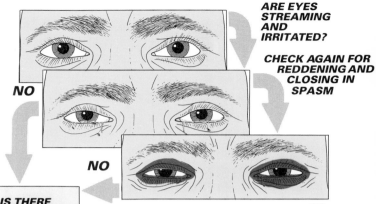

ARE EYES STREAMING AND IRRITATED?

CHECK AGAIN FOR REDDENING AND CLOSING IN SPASM

NO

NO

IS THERE SEVERE COUGHING?

YES

NO   **IS THERE RAPID AND DEEP BREATHING?**

TREAT FOR CHOKING AGENT

NO   **YES**

If the eyes are closing and weeping, look for reddening of the skin and blisters, especially in the hairline and behind the ears. Check for hoarseness of the voice and ask the casualty if he has a burning sensation in the lungs and a feeling of having a fever.

NO   **YES**

TREAT FOR BLOOD AGENT

UNKNOWN AGENT: EVACUATE CASUALTY TO MEDICAL AID

TREAT FOR BLISTER AGENT

FIRST AID FOR NERVE AGENT POISONING

1 When you are sure that a nerve agent is poisoning the casualty you must act quickly to save his life. NAPS tablets will buy time by building up resistance to the agent, but will not prevent death once contaminated. First, make sure both you and the casualty have the appropriate protection.

2 Take a Combopen from his haversack and inject one every 15 minutes until he recovers or until you have used his three combopens. Do not use your own. Replace the Combopens in his haversack so that others will know how many he has had. You may not need to use all of them, but the faster you get the first one in the better.

All nerve agents are lethal. They interfere with the nervous system and disrupt essential body functions such as breathing, vision and muscular coordination. Most of them are effective even in tiny quantities. They act very rapidly, especially if the agent has been breathed in because the poison is absorbed faster by lung tissue than by the skin. Nerve agents can also penetrate materials.

Types of nerve agent

Nerve agents can be divided into two groups – 'G' agents, which tend to be non-persistent, and 'V' agents, which are usually persistent.

The following agents are part of the Warsaw Pact chemical arsenal. But there are many others that you may encounter.

'G' Agents

Tabun (code letters GA)
Sarin (code letters GB)
Soman (code letters GD)

These are non-persistent.

'V' Agents

Codenames:
VX
VR55

These are persistent.

These agents can be delivered in the form of liquids, powders, aerosols or vapours.

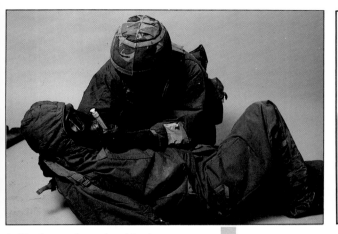

3 If he is conscious, show him the Combopen so that he knows what is going on, and reassure him. Make sure you inject into the muscle of his thigh and not into the maps in his map pocket.

4 If he is conscious, try to get him to take the Diazapan tablet in the top of the Combopen. Remember to decontaminate it fully before you do so. Do not try to give NAPS tablets.

5 If the casualty stops breathing, quickly and carefully decontaminate his face and give artificial respiration to restore lung function. If you know there is a vapour hazard use the portable resuscitator or Holger Nielsen method. If there is no vapour hazard (i.e. a non-persistent agent was used in the attack and has dispersed) then you can use mouth-to-mouth.

6 Evacuate the casualty to medical aid as soon as tactically possible.

Police Sniper Rifles

Left: Israeli police forces are equipped with the excellent sniper version of the 7.62-mm Galil. The weapon is a little heavy for police use and features folding stock with cheek piece, a superb Nimrod scope, bipod and 35-round magazines!

Below: A scoped-up and reworked SLR is capable of acceptable sniper accuracy out to around 600 metres in the hands of a competent shot. The Home Office went through a phase of imposing military weapons on police forces, but common sense has now largely prevailed and individual police forces can pick the weapon best suited to their needs.

The 1960s saw the arrival of the psychotic sniper in the USA, men who took to a high point with a rifle and shot at anyone in sight — and, as a result, police forces had to think of using snipers in retaliation.

But, as far as crime goes, what America thinks today the rest of the world thinks tomorrow. Over the past 20 years virtually every country has suffered from snipers, terrorists and similar disastrous affairs that can usually be dealt with only by accurate and lethal gunfire.

The Parker Hale T4 is a very solid long-range 7.62-mm bolt action which is again a bit cumbersome for vaulting over walls and running across roofs with. The heavy barrel makes it good to shoot from prone, but a little tiring from other positions.

The long shot

The requirement of a police sniper is somewhat different to that of a military sniper. The military sniper needs a weapon with which he can hit hard and accurately at long range. His targets are never less than 600 metres away, and in most cases the range is in excess of 1,000 metres. For this you require a heavy bullet and high muzzle velocity so that the trajectory is as flat as possible, the time of flight short, and the terminal energy sufficient to kill at the longest ranges.

The service 5.56mm rifle is outclassed in this sort of contest; the light bullet and high velocity are fine out to 300 or 400 metres, but after that the limitations begin to show up and the accuracy is nowhere near what is required for sniping. Moreover at long ranges the 5.56mm bullet simply does not have the residual energy to ensure maximum effect.

As a result, military sniping rifles are usually designed around an old-style full-power cartridge, such as the 7.62mm NATO, the 7.92mm Mauser or the 7.62×51 Soviet. Indeed, some firms have designed them to fire non-military rounds such as the .300 Winchester Magnum, claiming that these give better consistency and accuracy than out-of-the-box service ammunition.

Close-in sniping

But the police sniper is rarely interested in 1,000 metre shots; his problem is the terrorist holding a hostage in an airport or building, or the crazy sniper on a roof-top, or the cornered gunman in a building site.

None of these is likely to be more than 300 metres away, and the police sniper's principal problem is not so

much range as simply getting into a position where he can see his target without exposing himself. Thus the logical conclusion is that the full-power sniping rifle is over-powered for police use and something lighter and smaller could be sufficiently effective.

But, like every argument about weapons, it all comes back to the ammunition. You cannot be certain that shots over 300 metres will never be needed, so you take out insurance

by adopting the full-calibre sniping rifle anyway. There were police forces in the past who used things like .220 Swift and .275 Rigby sporting rifles for their precision requirements, and very successfully too. But today anything outside the standard calibres is virtually unusable unless you choose to hand-load or pay exorbitant prices. Police forces generally look askance at such solutions.

So it comes back to the military-pattern sniper, though perhaps with

US police forces and SWAT teams favour the Remington 700 bolt action sporting rifle, which is relatively light and fast-handling. The 700 was modified for use by US Marine Corps snipers in Vietnam and designated the M40A1. It has a fibreglass stock and heavy barrel.

some refinements. A good example is the Steyr Police Rifle. Steyr-Mannlicher produced an excellent military sniping rifle in the 1960s, calling it the SSG69. This uses the Mannlicher-Schoenauer rotary magazine, a turn-

Left: A German border police sergeant demonstrates the Mauser sniper rifle Model 66, as used by GSG 9. The weapon uses the Mauser front-locking short action and has an adjustable trigger, cheek piece and recoil pad.

Above: The mighty Mini 14 is a cheap and effective urban counter-sniper rifle for short- and medium-range work. The synthetic stock is as supplied to certain UK police forces. It cannot compete with 7.62 at long range, but is useful for most police encounters.

Inside the SSG 69

Foresight
This is a conventional protected post. The iron sights are only intended for emergency use if the scope is damaged.

Bore
The Steyr process also produces a slightly tapered bore towards the muzzle, which enhances accuracy.

Kahles ZF 69 telescope
Not surprisingly, the lens quality in these scopes is excellent and they can be internally adjusted to 800m in 100 increments to eliminate the need to hold over targets. The sights are attached to the rib cut in the receiver by clamped rings. In theory, you can remove and refit the scope quickly without altering the zero of the weapon.

Rear sight
This is a flip-up 'V' notch that can be drifted for windage.

The Model 69 is now the standard sniping rifle of the Austrian army. The rifle's full title is 'Steyr-Männlicher-Scharfschützengewehr. The Steyr police rifle is basically the same as the SSG with an extra-heavy barrel, an oversize match bolt handle and an adjustable shooting sling fitted in a fore-end rail. A 6×42 scope is fitted as standard.

receiver

receiver cut-out

breech bolt

Sling swivel

stock

Magazine
This is the standard spool-type rotary magazine seen on Steyr-Männlicher sporting rifles, but a 10-round detachable box magazine can be fitted.

Barrel
The barrel is interesting as it is made by a process of cold forging. This system of making barrels was developed by Steyr and involves placing the tube that is to become the barrel over a steel bar, which has rifling raised in relief on it. A series of hammers then hammers the outside so that the outer contours of the barrel are formed and hardened. At the same time, the rifling is hammered onto the inside surface and hardened. This cold forging process has been adopted by other rifle manufacturers.

bolt handle

magazine rotor

five rounds of 7.62-mm ammunition

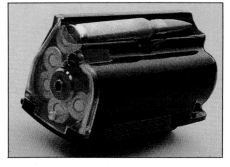

The rotary magazine ensures reliable functioning and the see-through plastic plate allows a quick inspection of ammunition state.

bolt action, and has a plastic stock, usually coloured olive drab.

The Police Rifle starts from the same basic action but uses the heavy barrel from the Steyr UIT Match rifle, the bolt with extended handle from the same source, adds a bipod, does away with iron sights and uses a 6×42 telescope as standard. Chambered for the 7.62 mm NATO round, this is as accurate as most shooters can hope for and it represents the pattern of how basic military weapons can be modified for

the less arduous requirements of police work.

Old hat?

But why, you may ask, does this excellent rifle rely upon a mechanism relatively unchanged since the turn of the century? For the Steyr-Mannlicher of 1969 used the same bolt and magazine as the Mannlicher-Schoe-

An Austrian police sniper team equipped with the SSG. The rifle is accurate enough to place 10 shots in a 400-mm group at 800 metres with RWS target ammo. At more realistic police ranges the rifle will group 10 rounds in 90mm at 300 metres and put five rounds into 15mm at 100 metres.

nauer of 1903 – with which the Greek Army was equipped until World War II.

Why not something more modern, a semi-automatic of some sort? After all, Steyr make the AUG, a classic automatic weapon, which is in wide use.

The answer is difficult, but it comes back to the primeval belief that semi-automatics are not as accurate as bolt-actions. And there is some warrant for this belief. The standard military rifle is not a precision weapon, by any measure; it is built to reach a specified standard of accuracy but, more important, it is built to withstand a battering that would make most rifles fall

Above: A close-up of the SSG demonstrates the advantages of the clear back to the 10-round magazine. Note that the safety catch is pushed forward off safe, revealing the red dot behind it, and the pin protruding from the rear of the bolt shows the weapon is cocked.

Ring mounts

Firing pin

Firing pin spring

Bolt

Bent

Plug breech bolt
The bolt is manually operated by moving through 60 degrees. The lock-up is achieved using six symmetrically arranged rear locking lugs. Rear lock-up allows a shorter bolt movement than the Mauser front locking system, but has always been less popular as the whole length of the bolt is stressed instead of just the bolt head. It could also be argued that the cut-out on the right side of the weapon in front of the locking shoulders weakens the weapon. However, Steyr have lengthened and strengthened the receiver so that the barrel receiver group is very rigid.

Spacers
Correct eye relief is essential. The SSG has adjustable butt length by adding the correct number of spacers.

...ve-shot magazine
...e rotary magazine is ...sily removed by ...essing in the magazine ...se on both sides of the ...dy forward of the trigger ...ard.

...m NATO round
...should not use ...ammunition as it is ...most accurate ... Top quality ...cial target ...tion will ...ably improve the ...capacity of the ...Home loading ...uce better results, ...an tailor the cartridge to the gun down to the last grain of powder and find the most accurate combination of bullet shape and weight and powder type. This is perhaps unrealistic for UK police forces, but is practised by some US police snipers.

Trigger guard

Trigger adjusting screw

Sear lever

Bolt stop
The bolt is removed by pulling back the bolt and then pressing the trigger, which holds the bolt stop down, allowing the bolt to be removed from the receiver. Further stripping for normal cleaning is not usually required.

Sling swivel
The sling is a useful aid to stability, but if you shoot with a sling you must zero with the sling. The sling is a must on police rifles as you could need both hands to climb into position.

to pieces. Reliability takes first place, so accuracy comes second, and when people tried to make the first semi-automatics shoot accurately they found them lacking.

Today, 40 years on, the production problems have been overcome, and it is now quite possible to make mass-produced semi-automatic actions that will shoot accurately enough to be sniping rifles. Heckler & Koch use the same delayed blowback action in their hunting rifles as they do in their military rifles, and they are excellent weapons.

But there is still a reluctance to place faith in a semi-auto for sniping. Bearing in mind that, among others, the standard Soviet Dragunov sniper, the Galil, the German H&K PSG-1 and Walther WA2000 are all semi-autos, it has to be said that there is a certain amount of reactionary prejudice.

How it looks

So far as police forces are concerned, though, they have another reason for avoiding military semi-automatics: appearance. Some foreign forces don't care; but the British and some others have no wish to be seen as

The SSG field-stripped. To strip the weapon, remove the magazine and open the bolt by rotating upwards and pulling it back to the limit of travel. Then pull the trigger to pull the bolt out backwards. Note the safety catch must be off. The bolt can be stripped further if required.

The Steyr Police rifle fitted with the UIT heavy barrel is even more accurate than the military version. Note also the over-large bolt handle to avoid fumbling; chances are if you do need a second shot, it will be taken under considerable stress.

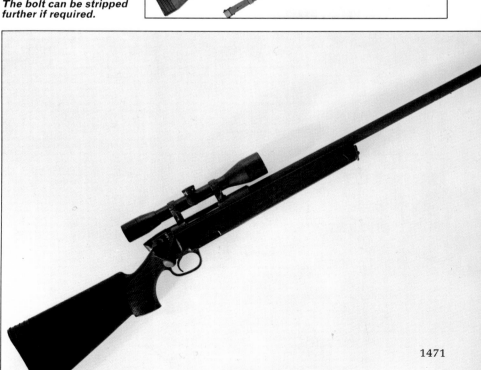

Full metal jacket versus soft point ammunition: the real problem with police use of 7.62-mm NATO weapons is the chance of overpenetration. 7.62 will cheerfully motor through the intended target and on into innocent bystanders. It can also ricochet and cause casualties.

Full metal jacket ammunition (on the left) does not expand on impact and provides a continuing hazard unless you are sure of your backstop. The lighter semi-jacketed soft point (right) mushrooms on hitting the target, doing considerably more damage.

some sort of oppressive para-military force carrying what look like military weapons.

For this reason, a wood-stocked bolt action, basically a sporting rifle, is favoured for police work in many places. Even some of the specialised weapons – the Steyr, the Beretta Sniper, the FN Sniper – have the appearance of 'civilian' weapons until you look closer.

There is, of course, a highly practical reason for the military to use semi-auto rifles; after firing a semi-auto it reloads, and the sniper doesn't have to move his arm to work a bolt and thus, possibly, reveal his position. He is not there for just one shot; he hopes to

Battlefield Evaluation: comparing

Steyr Police Rifle

Specification:
Cartridge: 17.62 mm×51 NATO
Weight: 4.2 kg
Length: 135 mm
Barrel length: 650 mm
Magazine: 5-round rotary or 10-round box magazine

This is a modified Steyr SSG using a heavy match-type barrel and fitted with a bipod for steadiness. The usual magazine is a five-round spool which can be slipped out and examined through a transparent backplate so that you can see how much ammunition is left. Alternatively, there is a 10-round conventional box magazine available. The stock is a black plastic material and the standard sight is a 6×42 Kahles telescope.

Assessment
Reliability   ★★★★
Accuracy   ★★★★
Age   ★
Worldwide users   ★★★★

The Steyr is good for police use but may be beyond the budget of some forces, and is a little heavy.

Parker Hale Model 85

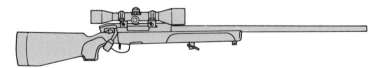

Specification:
Cartridge: 7.62 mm×51 NATO
Weight: 5 kg
Length: 1150 mm
Barrel length: 700 mm
Magazine: 10-round box

Parker Hale have been in the competition and hunting rifle business for years, and their Model 85 reflects their experience. Basically a Mauser action with refinements, it has a fairly heavy barrel, a trigger adjustable for weight and pull and a walnut stock with a screw to take a bipod. The barrel is free-floating and the muzzle can be threaded to take a flash hider. Iron sights are fitted and a 6×44 telescopic sight is standard.

Assessment
Reliability   ★★★★
Accuracy   ★★★★
Age   ★
Worldwide users   ★★

The Parker Hale can match the accuracy of the Steyr and is considerably cheaper.

Beretta Sniper

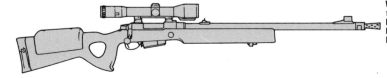

Specification:
Cartridge: 7.62 mm×51 NATO
Weight: 7.2 kg (with telescope and bipod)
Length: 1165 mm
Barrel length: 586 mm
Magazine: 5-round box

Another bolt-action rifle in 7.62-mm NATO calibre, the Beretta is recognisable by its thumb-hole stock, bipod and bell-mouthed flash hider. The bipod mounting can also contain an harmonic balancer, a device which damps out barrel vibration to give superbly consistent shooting. The rifle has iron sights but the receiver has the NATO STANAG 2426 mount which accepts any NATO day or night sight; the standard sight is a Zeiss Diavari zoom telescope.

Assessment
Reliability   ★★★★
Accuracy   ★★★★
Age   ★
Worldwide users   ★★★★

The Beretta is a very finely crafted weapon, but has not yet won any contracts outside Italy.

make three or four.

The police sniper, on the other hand, rarely needs more than one good shot to do what is required, and reloading is no problem. So, once again, the bolt action is perfectly adequate for his needs. And, the final clinching argument for most police forces: accurate bolt-actions are cheaper than accurate semi-automatics.

US SWAT teams use Armalites firing the 5.56-mm round: the round is accurate over normal police engagement ranges and is less of a hazard to innocent bystanders than 7.62-mm. It also helps if the felon has a can of Coke in each hand before you issue your challenge!

police sniper rifles

Heckler and Koch PSG-1

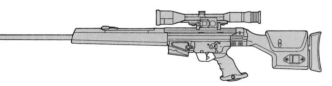

This uses exactly the same semi-automatic mechanism as all the H & K military rifles, a delayed blowback using a roller locking system. It has a heavy barrel and a set trigger giving excellent control. The butt is adjustable for length and height and there is an unusual hand stop on the pistol grip so that you take the same grip every time. No iron sights are fitted; the standard scope is a 6×42.

Specification:
Cartridge: 7.62 mm×51 NATO
Weight: 8.29 kg with a 5 round magazine
Length: 1208 mm
Barrel length: 650 mm
Magazine: 5- or 20-round box

Assessment
Reliability   ★★★★
Accuracy   ★★★★
Age   ★
Worldwide users   ★★★★

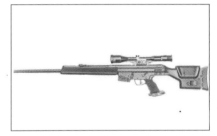

The PSG-1 as a self-loader has some advantages over bolt action weapons in counter-terrorist operations.

Mauser SP66

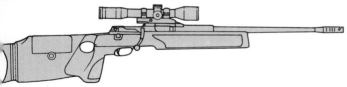

A bolt-action rifle inevitably using the short-throw Mauser action. The free floating heavy barrel is fitted with a muzzle brake and the butt is fully adjustable. There are no iron sights and the NATO mount is used, carrying a Zeiss 1.5-6×42 zoom telescope as standard. The SP66 is generally considered to be one of the finest compromises between accuracy and ruggedness, with the balance tilted towards the former.

Specification:
Cartridge: 7.62 mm×51 NATO
Weight: not revealed
Length: not revealed
Barrel length: 680 mm
Magazine: 3-round internal magazine

Assessment
Reliabilty   ★★★★
Accuracy   ★★★★
Age   ★
Worldwide users   ★★★★

The Mauser is an extremely well made and expensive rifle with performance equal to that of the Steyr.

Galil Sniper

The sniping version of the Israeli Army's standard rifle, this uses a semi-automatic mechanism based on the Kalashnikov's rotating bolt and gas action. The trigger is more precise than the standard pattern, the barrel is heavier and carries a muzzle brake, and there is a bipod mounted well back where you can adjust it without attracting too much attention. Iron sights are fitted but the standard sight is a 6×40 Nimrod telescope on a non-standard mount fitted to the side of the receiver.

Specification:
Cartridge: 7.62 mm×51 NATO
Weight: 6.4 kg including bipod and sling
Length: 1115 mm
Barrel length: 508 mm
Magazine: 20-round magazine

Assessment
Reliablity   ★★★★
Accuracy   ★★★★
Age   ★
Worldwide users   ★★

The Galil will not match the long-range accuracy of the Steyr police rifle.

Panzer Recce! The Spähpanzer Luchs

*Right: A Luchs armoured car probes cautiously towards the edge of a wood during a **NATO** exercise. An 8×8 all-wheel driven vehicle, the Luchs is an exceptionally mobile AFV.*

Few countries in the world appreciate the significance of timely reconnaissance as much as the Federal German Republic, situated as it is at the centre of any potential East-West confrontation. Although the superpowers have recently entered into much publicised talks to diminish the threat of a nuclear holocaust, nothing has been done to reduce conventional arsenals. Indeed, with the introduction of new self-propelled tracked artillery and the T-64 B main battle tank, the Third Shock Army, the main Soviet threat to the North German plain, is far stronger than ever.

In any future confrontation the Warsaw Pact would ruthlessly exploit weaknesses in the NATO front. Operational Manoeuvre Groups, not dissimilar to the Nazi Panzer Divisions of 1940, would sweep behind the lines, rupturing the defences and causing panic among the civilian population.

The West German Government is acutely aware that such battles would take place on its land and has not forgotten the atrocities committed by the Red Army during its last incursion

onto German soil. Accordingly the 'Territorial' units defending its rear echelons are highly mobile and their headquarters are served constantly with current intelligence to enable them to pre-empt an enemy break-through.

The modern commander has an infinite variety of intelligence gathering agencies available to him. Many of

*Above: The large size of the Luchs is readily apparent when all four crew members have their hatches open. **Note** the radio operator/rear driver at the back: he has a complete set of controls and can drive the vehicle swiftly out of trouble.*

these, notably the spy-plane, satellite and electronic counter-measure systems, are modern and highly complex. Others, personified by the infantry recce patrol, are as old as the army itself.

The German army introduced a series of revolutionary scout cars before World War II. Relying on speed rather than armoured protection and with just enough firepower to extricate themselves from danger, these vehicles acted as the eyes of the Panzer Divisions. As the war progressed and the Allies began to construct their own, they followed a similar pattern with a four-wheel-drive chassis, armoured hull and rotating turret mounting a light-calibre quick-

A column of Luchs armoured cars assembles for action. Note the door in the hull side between the two sets of wheels and the propellers on the hull rear, which power the Luchs at up to 9km/h in the water.

firing weapon. The modern reconnaissance vehicle typified by the Luchs is a direct descendant of these armoured cars.

Development

Development of the Luchs began in 1964 when the German Ministry of Defence began to implement plans for the creation of a new family of military vehicles to include an 8×8 amphibious reconnaissance vehicle, 4×4 and 6×6 amphibious load carriers and a series of trucks. Daimler-Benz and a consortium lead by Krupp, MAN and Rheinstal began the immediate development of rival prototypes. In 1973 a contract for the production of the Luchs reconnaissance vehicle was awarded to Rheinstahl. Production began in May 1975 and by the end of 1977 408 models had entered service.

Description

The all-welded hull of the Luchs is proof against small arms fire and shell splinters, although its comparatively thin armour would afford little protection to the four-man crew against a direct hit from the weapon systems of the latest generation MICVs.

The driver seated at the front-left of the hull is provided with a single-piece hatch cover opening to the right

A Luchs demonstrates its splendid suspension system. Although all eight wheels are steered, only the front four are normally used when travelling along a road. The vehicle's armour is necessarily thin but at least the front of the hull is very well sloped.

and is equipped with three periscopes offering a reasonable forward vision even when driving closed-down. Uniquely a second driver, who also acts as the radio operator, is situated facing rearwards behind the engine. Equipped with a similar configuration of single hatch cover and three periscopes, when directed the rear driver is capable of taking over complete control of the vehicle.

Whether the obvious theoretical advantages of a second driver are as apparent in reality is a matter for debate. In action the rear driver will be constantly attending to the stream of signals associated with a reconnaissance vehicle once its presence has been compromised and he is more than likely to be severely disorientated; a problem well known to

mechanised infantrymen operating from the rear of enclosed armoured personnel carriers! It is therefore highly unlikely that he will be able to assume immediate responsibility for charting a rearward passage to safety without considerable assistance from the commander. Well trained crews of conventionally driven reconnaissance vehicles practise the art of speedy withdrawal incessantly, with the result that an experienced commander-driver team can reverse their vehicle immediately and at speed even when the latter is totally unsighted.

Mobility

The engine, transmission, air filter and oil filter, located together at the rear of the turret, are mounted as a

The Luchs suspension system

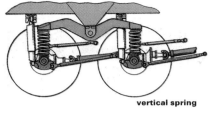

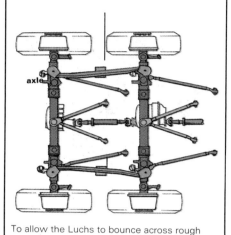

To allow the Luchs to bounce across rough ground at a suitably vigorous pace, the suspension system consists of four rigid axles supported by longitudinal bars. Each wheel station has a vertical coil spring and hydraulic shock absorber.

vertical spring

axle

Inside the Luchs

The Luchs is directly descended from the excellent 8×8 armoured cars used by the German army in World War II. The requirement to be fully amphibious led to a large hull, which makes the Luchs one of the largest recce vehicles in service. Production has been completed and the Luchs has not been exported.

7.62-mm machine-g
A Rheinmetall MG3 GP
is fixed to a skate
mounting above the
commander's hatch. Its
value as an anti-aircraft
weapon is rather limited
and to engage enemy
infantry the commander
would have to make
himself vulnerable to
small-arms fire.

Gunner

Driver's periscopes
The central periscope can
be replaced by a passive
night periscope.

Driver

Hull frontal armour
This is proof against
weapons up to 20-mm
calibre: the primary Soviet
opponent is the BRDM
armoured car which
carries a 14.5-mm
machine-gun.

Trim vane
This is erected
hydraulically before the
Luchs enters the water.

complete unit to facilitate speedy removal from the vehicle under field or other adverse conditions. The engine employed is the well proven Daimler-Benz Type OM 403 VA, 10-cylinder, 4-stroke with fuel injection and turbocharger. Capable of developing 390 hp with diesel fuel and 300 hp when used with petrol, this thoroughly reliable engine enables the Luchs to attain a top road speed of 90 km/h, both forwards and backwards, and to accelerate from 0/80 km/h in 65 seconds, a not inconsiderable feat for a vehicle weighing 19,500 kg.

The Luchs is fully amphibious with the aid of two propellers, one on each side of the hull rear, being capable of a top speed in current-free water of 10 km/h. Preparation is virtually

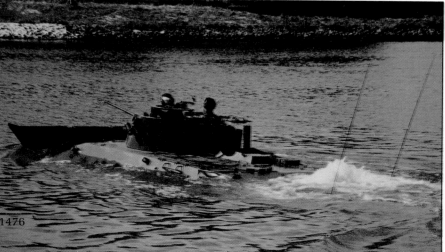

A Luchs heads across still water with trim vane erected. Like the Soviets, the Germans believe recce vehicles should be truly amphibious and thus able to cross a water obstacle without elaborate preparations.

Smoke rocket dischargers
Four are mounted on each side of the turret.

Turret armour
This is proof against weapons up to 20-mm calibre all round.

Searchlight
This can be used in infra-red mode and it follows the same elevation as the 20-mm cannon.

20-mm Rheinmetall Mk 20 Rh202 cannon
This is the same weapon as mounted on the Marder MICV. It uses a dual feed and ejects the empty cases and cartridge links to the right of the turret. It provides a hail of anti-personnel fire, but its value against armoured vehicles is limited.

Radio operator/rear driver
The unique feature is the second driving station in the hull rear, which allows the radio operator to get the vehicle out of trouble fast. The Luchs can travel backwards as fast as it goes forwards, which is very handy in the cut-and-thrust world of armoured recce.

Hull side armour
The side and rear of the Luchs are sufficiently armoured to keep out small arms fire and shell splinters, but can be penetrated by heavy machine-gun or cannon fire.

Hull door

Below: The opposition – a column of BMPs rumble through open woodland. While the Luchs can fight its way past BRDM armoured cars, Soviet recce includes MICVs and even tanks against which a 20-mm cannon is of little value. Whether the Luchs will be re-fitted with a more powerful weapon remains open to speculation.

negligible, a trim vane being erected hydraulically by the driver before the vehicle enters the water. Steering, effected by swivelling the propellers, is adequate but not excellent.

Aided by the driver's ability to select either the front four wheels, rear four wheels or all eight wheels for steering, the Luchs has an excellent cross-country capability. With a maximum road range of 800 km coupled with the capacity to climb gradients of 60 per cent, traverse trenches 1.9 metres deep and overcome vertical obstacles of 0.6 metres, it remains, despite its age, one of the most versa-

Just how closely the Luchs follows the design of earlier German armoured cars can be seen from this picture of an Afrika Korps Sd Kfz 231 (8-Rad). This too, had a 20-mm cannon and a machine-gun, but was not amphibious.

tile reconnaissance vehicles in current service.

The Luchs is in every respect a reconnaissance vehicle and as such has not been designed to enter into fire fights. The two-man power operated turret is situated behind the driver. The main armament is a 20 mm Rheinmetall Mk 20 Rh 202 cannon, identical to that mounted on the Marder MICV. Capable of accepting high explosive or armour piercing shells, the gun is extremely accurate and reliable. However, the Luchs lacks the sophisticated automatic loading system found in the Marder and as such, unless it were to attain a first round kill, would be no match for the

Battlefield Evaluation: comparing

Luchs

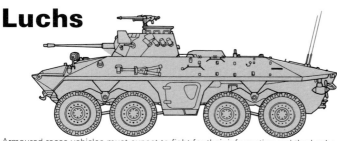

Armoured recce vehicles must expect to fight for their information and the Luchs is well equipped to take on Soviet wheeled recce like the BRDM-2 armoured cars. Unfortunately the Soviets also tend to attach tanks to their recce formations.

Specification:
Crew: 4
Combat weight: 19.5 tonnes
Road speed: 90 km/h
Power to weight ratio: 20 hp/tonne
Length: 7.74 m
Height: 2.1 m
Armament: 1×20-mm cannon; 1×7.62-mm machine-gun

Assessment
Firepower   ★★
Protection   ★★
Age   ★★★
Worldwide users   ★

The Luchs suits the West German army's recce needs, but has won no export orders.

Renault VBC 90

This is one of several French 6×6 armoured cars which are notable for their heavy firepower. Substantially lighter than the Luchs, the VBC 90 is faster but not amphibious. Oman operates a handful of VBC 90s and the French Gendarmerie bought 28 vehicles in the early 1980s, but it has not achieved major export sales.

Specification:
Crew: 3
Combat weight: 12.8 tonnes
Road speed: 92 km/h
Power to weight ratio: 17.96 hp/tonne
Length: 5.63 m
Height: 2.52 m (turret top)
Armament: 1×90-mm gun; 2×7.62-mm machine-guns

Assessment
Firepower   ★★★★
Protection   ★
Age   ★★
Worldwide users   ★

The VBC 90 is one of a series of light AFVs produced by Renault, but has not achieved great success.

Panhard ERC

The ERC replaces the Panhard AML 60 and AML 90 in the recce formations of the French Rapid Deployment Force Divisions. The 90-mm gun fires HE, HEAT and APFSDS as well as smoke and canister. Alternative weapon fits include 25-mm cannon, twin 20-mm AA guns, six SATCP surface-to-air missiles or a 60-mm mortar. Many French units serving overseas have received ERCs including troops in Djibouti, Gabon and the Ivory Coast.

Specification: Sagaie 2
Crew: 3
Combat weight: 10 tonnes
Road speed: 110 km/h
Power to weight ratio: 19.6 hp/tonne
Length: 5.57 m
Height: 2.32 m
Armament: 1×90-mm gun; 2×7.62-mm machine-guns

Assessment
Firepower   ★★★★
Protection   ★
Age   ★
Worldwide users   ★★

The French Force d'Action Rapide has 108 amphibious and air-portable Panhard ERC Sagaies.

latest generation of Soviet armoured vehicles such as the BMP-2. A Rheinmetall 7.62 mm MG3 machine-gun is mounted on a ring mount over the commander's hatch.

Still in service

The Luchs is fitted with an NBC system and automatic fire-extinguishing system as well as a highly versatile heater capable of blowing hot air over the engine if required. Unlike many German vehicles of its generation Luchs was never exported, nor were any variants produced. Nevertheless, 408 models remain in Bundeswehr service and show no signs of being replaced.

The Luchs can accelerate to 50 mph in just over a minute, which is good going for an armoured car, and it has a good cross-country performance. The West German army has about 400 Luchs armoured cars in service.

the Luchs with its rivals

ENGESA EE-9 Cascavel

Successfully sold all over Africa and South America, this Brazilian armoured car is likely to crop up in the odd news bulletin for years to come. Later production models sold to Iraq have a laser rangefinder with a protective shutter which closes when you fire the main armament. They also use the Soviet 12.7-mm DshKM machine-gun in favour of the Browning .50-calibre.

Specification:
Crew: 3
Combat weight: 13.7 tonnes
Road speed: 100 km/h
Power to weight ratio: 15.5 hp/tonne
Length: 5.2 m
Height: 2.6 m
Armament: 1×90-mm gun; 1×90.7-mm and 1×7.62-mm machine-guns

Assessment
Firepower ★★★★
Protection ★★
Age ★★
Worldwide users ★★★★

ENGESA have recently donated an EE-9 Cascavel to the tank museum at Bovington.

RAM

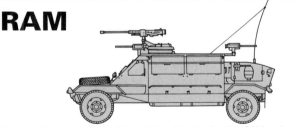

Developed by a subsidiary of Israeli Aircraft Industries, the RAM series of light recce vehicles is a comprehensive range of 4×4 vehicles offered for export. Moroccan forces have bought an undisclosed number for their continuing struggle against Polisario guerrillas. Anti-tank armament can be either a 106-mm recoilless rifle or TOW missile launcher. A self-propelled AA gun version using twin 20-mm cannon is also available.

Specification: RAM V-2L long
Crew: 2+6
Combat weight: 6 tonnes
Road speed: 96 km/h
Power to weight ratio: undisclosed
Length: 5.5 m
Height: 2 m
Armament: 1×.50-cal and 2×7.62-mm machine-guns

Assessment
Firepower ★★
Protection ★
Age ★
Worldwide users ★★

The Israeli RAM continues the jeep tradition of fast, 4×4 recce vehicles.

AML 90

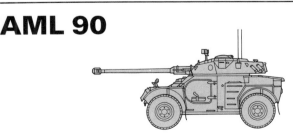

Since 1961 nearly 5,000 AML 90s have been built, making it one of the most successful post-war recce vehicles. Not amphibious, the basic AML 90 also lacks NBC protection and night fighting kit, although all these features are available as optional extras. The Argentines took a few of their AML 90s to the Falklands but they could not cope with the boggy ground and did not see action.

Specification:
Crew: 3
Combat weight: 5.5 tonnes
Road speed: 90 km/h
Power to weight ratio: 16.36 hp/tonne
Length: 3.79 m
Height: 2.07 m
Armament: 1×90-mm gun; 1×7.62-mm machine-gun

Assessment
Firepower ★★★
Protection ★★
Age ★★★★
Worldwide users ★★★★★

The AML 90 lacks the cross-country power and amphibious capability of the Luchs, but is better armed.

Beast From Brazil
The EE-9 Cascavel Armoured Car

Fast, powerful and readily available, the Cascavel armoured car is being sold all over the world by the flourishing Brazilian arms company, ENGESA. Brazil has cheerfully exported AFVs and rocket artillery to both sides in the Gulf War as well as to armies in Africa and Latin America. The first Cascavels appeared in 1972, produced for the Brazilian army. Since then some 2,500 have been manufactured and it is ENGESA's greatest success.

Armed with a 90-mm gun, the Cascavel is protected by an unusual dual-

A 90-mm round blasts downrange from Brazil's powerful EE-9 armoured car. The Cascavel fires a wide selection of ammunition, from conventional HEAT and HESH rounds to an anti-personnel canister round packed with 1,100 lead alloy balls. Although a fire control system is still at the development stage, some EE-9s supplied to Iraq and used in the Gulf war were fitted with a laser rangefinder.

Below: ENGESA also manufacture the EE-11 Urutu, a 6×6 armoured personnel carrier, and the two vehicles share many components, which greatly simplifies logistic support.

hardness armour configuration consisting of an outer layer of hard steel and inner layer of roll-bonded, heat-treated softer steel to afford maximum ballistic support. Increased protection is given to the frontal arc, and special attention has been paid to the threat posed by booby traps, grenades and Molotov cocktails, any of which could prove lethal to a crew operating in the confines of a jungle or, more probably, in a built-up area during a period of civil unrest.

The driver, who is provided with a single hatch cover opening to the right, sits in the front left of the hull. Everything possible has been done to make his life comfortable — his seat and steering wheel are adjustable, and there is a small windscreen and wiper that fold forward onto the glacis plate when not in use — but the three peri-

scopes in the top part of the glacis plate provide him with no more than 120° visibility when closed down, barely enough for operational purposes.

The Boomerang walking beam suspension, originally fitted to ENGESA 6×6 trucks, is versatile and efficient, consisting of a rigid axle connected to the hull by double leaf springs and telescopic dampers holding two lateral walking beams through which power is taken from the drive to the four rear wheels. Up to 2.95 ft of vertical travel has been built into the rear wheels, enabling the vehicle to keep them in contact with the ground at all times, which considerably enhances the vehicle's traction when operating in muddy, hilly conditions prevalent in parts of South America. As a refinement, the run-flat tyres will keep the Cascavel mobile for over 100 km even when fully deflated.

Optional equipment, including the air-conditioning system, heater, laser rangefinder, automatic fire extinguisher and active or passive night vision enhancements, are available and, when fitted, upgrade the Casca-vel considerably, bringing it up to European and United States standards.

Powerpack

A Detroit Diesel 6V-53N six-cylinder water-cooled diesel engine developing 212 hp at 2,800 rpm is normally fitted, although alternatives may be installed if required. The versatile and powerful Detroit engine is capable of a maximum road speed of 100 km/h, but is economical enough to give a maximum range of 880 km, far further than the vast majority of more

Right: Both the Brazilian army and their Marines use the Cascavel which, although not amphibious, can ford up to a meter of water. Note the driver's windscreen folded down on the glacis.

The Boomerang walking beam suspension, in which the rear wheels are capable of extreme vertical travel, gives the EE-9 excellent performance over rough ground. The same system is used on ENGESA's range of 6×6 tactical trucks.

sophisticated vehicles. Although not amphibious, the Cascavel can ford to a depth of 1 metre, can climb gradients of 60 per cent and overcome vertical obstacles of 0.6 metres. The engine, at the rear of the hull, is co-located with the Detroit Diesel MT 643 gearbox, which has four forward and one reverse gears. A purpose-built ENGESA transfer box splits the drive between the front and rear differentials, giving maximum traction and control whatever the speed and conditions.

Of prime importance when operating in adverse conditions, access to the engine is easily obtained via two large, hinged doors at the top rear of the hull. Although the engine cannot be removed as quickly and easily as in the case of many armoured vehicles of European construction, particularly the French AML or British CVR(T) series, this is not in itself a problem in South American armies, which can-

not always rely on advanced mechanical assistance in the field. The engine design is basic enough and access adequate to enable most immediate problems to be resolved.

A double 24-volt electrical system is fitted, one part of which generates power for the engine and turret. The other acts as a fail-safe back-up to start the engine after long periods of static radio operations – again a concept sadly lacking in many more sophisticated and far more expensive designs.

Firepower

Initial production models of the Cascavel were fitted with a French H 90 turret armed with a 90-mm gun similar to that equipping the highly successful AML 90. Current models, however, boast the domestically produced ENGESA ET-90 turret and EC-90 gun. Designed with the export market in mind, both have been installed successfully in the Greek Steyr 4K 7FA APC, have been trialled with the Vickers Valkyr and will fit a wide series of other tracked or wheeled armoured cars and personnel carriers.

The all-welded steel turret, 16mm thick at the front and 8.5mm thick at the sides, rear and top, is proof against all small-arms fire and anything other than a direct hit from 105-mm light artillery, and the gun is capable of penetrating the protective armour of any APC and of most reconnaissance vehicles. This makes the Cascavel a formidable fighting machine in any Third World conflict, in which it is likely that expensive and sophisticated modern main battle tanks will not be deployed.

The turret itself is comparatively low but is surmounted by a huge cupola, presumably inspired by the French AMX design, above the com-

EC-90-III 90-mm gun
The Brazilian version of the Belgian Cockerill 90-mm gun, this fires HEAT rounds with a maximum effective range of 2000m, although an APDSFS round has now been developed, This will substantially improve the Cascavel's anti-armour capability.

Muzzle brake

Driver's windscreen
This folds down across t glacis and has an integra windscreen wiper.

Dual-hardness armour
Protected over the frontal area by up to 16mm of steel armour, the Cascavel is proof against small-arms fire and machine-guns.

Combat tyres
The tyres are run-flats and enable the Cascavel to travel up to 100km on deflated tyres.

The commander's cupola stands 2.6 metres off the ground, making an imposing sight but a potentially good target. The Browning .50 cal, mounted by the cupola, is fitted in a similar manner to the Soviet 12.7-mm AA machine-guns. Ground clearance is 34cm to the front axle and 50cm to the hull.

mander's seat on the left. Both the turret and cupola consist of an outer layer of hard steel and an inner layer of steel roll-bonded and heat-treated for enhanced ballistic protection.

The main armament consists of the Cockerill-designed, ENGESA-manufactured EC-90 gun with an elevation of +15°, depression of −8° and manual traverse through 360°. A powered system does exist as an expensive alternative.

An externally mounted 7.62-mm machine-gun, aimed and fired from within the safety of the turret, can be mounted onto the ENGESA ET-762 cupola and in certain instances can be replaced by the far more potent 12.7-mm M2 HB machine-gun mounted on a Soviet-style DShKM

Inside the Cascavel

The Cascavel was designed by ENGESA to meet the requirements of the Brazilian army. First production vehicles were armed with 37-mm guns removed from the ancient M3 Stuart light tanks acquired in the late 1940s. The next batch sported French H-90 turrets, but current production models have a Brazilian turret and the vehicle has been widely exported.

Browning .50-cal machine-gun
Shown here on the basic anti-aircraft mounting, other fittings are available, including one that allows the gun to be fired from inside the turret.

r rangefinder
rst Cascavels to carry r rangefinder carried e above the barrel, is mounting is rable to shrapnel and arms fire and they w built into the er's sight.

Commander's cupola

Commander

Smoke grenade launchers

Central tyre pressure regulator
The driver can adjust tyre pressure to suit the type of ground the vehicle is traversing. On roads the tyre pressure should be 4 kg/cm²; going cross country, 3 kg/cm²; and 2 kg/cm² on snow, mud or soft sand.

Boomerang suspension
With 90 cm vertical wheel travel, the walking beam suspension enables all four rear wheels to stay in contact with the ground, however rough the terrain. This contributes enormously to the Cascavel's cross-country performance.

anti-aircraft mantel.

Due to its comparatively small size, the turret is a mere 1.84 metres wide and 0.59 metres high. Storage space is at a premium, reducing the weapon-load to a rather unsatisfactory 24 rounds of main ammunition and 2,000 rounds of 7.62-mm for the machine-guns. This means frequent replenishment where possible or, more likely, strict ammunition conservation, a discipline rarely found among Third World armies.

Variants

Although a Mk V model of the Cascavel retro-fitted with a Mercedes-Benz OM 352 A diesel engine developing 190 hp at 2,800 rpm is available, no true variants exist. But a

The Cascavel has a laser rangefinder built into the gunner's sight (the hooded screen next to the cupola) instead of mounted over the gun. It is protected by a shutter which falls into place when you fire the main armament.

The EE-11 APC has the same dual-hardness armour, Boomerang suspension system and run-flat tyres as the EE-9. Both incorporate many commercially available automotive parts, which reduces manufacturing and operating costs. Just to confuse your vehicle recognition, ENGESA are now offering the EE-11 with the same turret as the EE-9.

number of optional extras are available, including a recently developed laser-rangefinder aimed through the gunner's sight and protected by a shutter when the main armament is fired to take the place of the externally mounted and therefore vulnerable external sight, and various radio installations.

The Cascavel does not have any form of NBC protection – presumably not a problem in the environments in which it is likely to operate – nor does it have the benefit of additional air conditioning, which would be of distinct benefit to crews operating in the uncompromising heat of the North African desert.

Battlefield Evaluation: comparing

ENGESA EE-9 Cascavel

The EE-9 is in service worldwide and has seen extensive action: Libya bought a batch of EE-9s and supplied them to its allies in Chad's interminable civil war; some were captured by French-backed forces, and are now used by the Chadian government forces; Iraq used EE-9s for armoured recce during the Gulf war. EE-9s have been supplied to many Latin American countries

Specification:
Crew: 3
Combat weight: 13.7 tonnes
Road speed: 100 km/h
Power to weight ratio: 15.5 hp/tonne
Length: 5.2 m
Height: 2.6 m
Armament: 1×90-mm gun; 1×7.62-mm machine-gun; 1×.50-cal machine-gun

Assessment
Firepower	★★★★
Protection	★★
Age	★★
Worldwide users	★★★

The Cascavel is one of ENGESA's most successful and widely exported armoured fighting vehicles.

FIAT-OTO Melara 6616

FIAT provides the hull and automotive parts for this armoured car while OTO-Melara supplies the turret and armament. It is used by the Italian paramilitary Carabinieri and has been supplied to Peru, Somalia and some undisclosed countries. Fully amphibious, it has numerous optional extras from NBC kit to air conditioning, and a 106-mm recoilless rifle on the turret roof.

Specification: (90 mm version)
Crew: 3
Combat weight: 8.2 tonnes
Road speed: 100 km/h
Power to weight ratio: 29.5 hp/tonne
Length: 5.37 m
Height: 2 m
Armament: 1×90-mm Mk III Cockerill gun; 1×7.62-mm machine-gun

Assessment
Firepower	★★★★
Protection	★★
Age	★★
Worldwide users	★★

The Fiat OTO-Melara 6614 can be armed with a 20-mm cannon or the same type of 90-mm gun as the EE-9.

VEC

Using many components of the BMR-600 APC, the VEC is the Spanish army's new recce vehicle. Spanish VECs are fitted with the OTO Melara T25 turret mounting a 25-mm cannon and co-axial 7.62-mm machine-gun, but the hull is compatible with other OTO Melara turrets including the same one as carried by the FIAT-OTO Melara 6614. The full spectrum of machine-guns, cannon or 90-mm Cockerill gun are offered on export versions of the VEC.

Specification:
Crew: 5
Combat weight: 13.75 tonnes
Road speed: 106 km/h
Power to weight ratio: 22.25 hp/tonne
Length: 6.25 m
Height: 2 m
Armament: 90-mm gun or 20/25-mm cannon plus 7.62-mm machine-gun

Assessment
Firepower	★★★★
Protection	★★
Age	★★
Worldwide use	★

The VEC Cavalry vehicle has the advantage of being fully amphibious.

To date, the EE-9 Cascavel has proved a great success. It shares many of its automotive parts with the EE-11 Urutu armoured personnel carrier, making a combined purchase financially attractive, and can be fitted with a smaller 300-mm recoil 90-mm gun and turret if required. By January 1984, 2,550 EE-9 Cascavel armoured cars had been produced and construction continues unabated. While the United States, France, Germany and the United Kingdom continue to produce complex combat vehicles beyond the pockets of smaller nations, weapons systems such as the Cascavel will always have an assured market.

*For the armies of most developing nations the Cascavel makes better sense than a second-hand main battle tank from **NATO** or the Warsaw Pact. However, many Third World manufacturers, including **ENGESA**, are now producing their own.*

the EE-9 Cascavel with its rivals

Commando Scout

The Scout takes a radically different approach to reconnaissance than large combat vehicles like the EE-9. Smaller and more agile, it has far greater range (1,287 km against 750 km for the EE-9). Its size precludes powerful cannon armament, but it can mount TOW anti-tank guided missiles, so it could take on the bigger opposition providing it initiated the engagement. The tyres are 'Commando Special' run-flat combat tubeless types, and it uses a four speed automatic transmission.

Specification:
Crew: 2 or 3
Combat weight: 7.2 tonnes
Road speed: 96 km/h
Power to weight ratio: 20.5 hp/tonne
Length: 4.69 m
Height: 2.23 m
Armament: 1 or 2×7.62-mm machine-guns and/or TOW missile launcher

Assessment
Firepower ★★★
Protection ★
Age ★
Worldwide users ★

For light armoured recce, the Scout is a nifty alternative.

MOWAG SPY

Sharing many components with the MOWAG 'Piranha' range, the SPY was developed for export only and has been sold in the Far East. It is a cheaper but less effective combat vehicle than the EE-9 type 6×6 vehicles, but you pays your money and you takes your choice. The hull will keep out 7.62-mm ball, and is shaped to deflect the blast from a mine. Turret traverse and weapon elevation are manual.

Specification:
Crew: 3
Combat weight: 7.5 tonnes
Road speed: 110 km/h
Power to weight ratio: 27 hp/tonne
Length: 4.5 m
Height: 1.66 m
Armament: 1×12.7-mm and 1×7.62-mm machine-guns

Assessment
Firepower ★★
Protection ★
Age ★
Worldwide users ★

*The SPY uses many of the same components as the **MOWAG** Piranha range of armoured vehicles.*

AMX-10RC

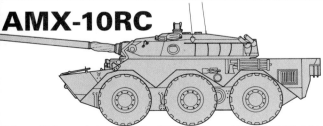

Fully amphibious and air-portable, the AMX-10RC is used by 6e DLB (6th light armoured division) along with VAB APCs armed with HOT missiles. The combination gives the French Rapid Deployment Force a powerful mobile striking force able to take on enemy armour. With its semi-automatic 105-mm gun and fully stabilised turret to allow for shooting on the move, the AMX-10RC is a well-balanced combination of mobility and firepower.

Specification:
Crew: 4
Combat weight: 16 tonnes
Road speed: 85 km/h
Power to weight ratio: 16.45 hp/tonne
Length: 6.3 m
Height: 2.7 m
Armament: 1×105-mm gun; 1×7.62-mm machine-gun

Assessment
Firepower ★★★★★
Protection ★★
Age ★★
Worldwide users ★★

The AMX-10RC is much more capable than the Cascavel, but this superior performance is reflected in the price.

Survival in the Treeline

The skills you learn in your Arctic training have a far wider application than Norway. Austrian mountain troops train for war in the snow-capped Alpine regions. Even UK weather can be severe enough to provide a serious test of these skills.

The Arctic terrain of northern Norway restricts freedom of movement and is well suited to defence by small units. On the other hand, transport of logistic support and reinforcements is very difficult. Even if you do receive reinforcements you will still be heavily outnumbered by Warsaw Pact forces, and so there is a good chance that, either alone or with your unit, you will find yourself in a struggle for survival as you try to evade the enemy.

If you are in the treeline, you may find that the snow is not deep enough to build snow shelters, but you can make brushwood shelters. There are five basic designs which you can adapt to suit your purpose or the conditions:

1 Single lean-to shelter
2 Double lean-to shelter
3 Wigwam-style shelter
4 Tree pit shelter
5 Fallen tree shelter

Basic building rules

The lean-to designs are the simplest, but the wigwam is the best, warmest and most comfortable. The tree pit and fallen tree are best used in tactical situations. If you have these basic designs in your mind, you can adapt them to most circumstances.

Build the main wall with its back to the prevailing wind, and weave it thickly with whatever wood or branches are available. A small wall can be built downwind to provide reflection for the heat from a fire. You can use snow to reinforce the woven wall, but it should not go too high up or it will melt into the 'bivi' from the roof.

If possible, dig down to ground level for the fire. If this is impossible, build a good solid firebase of mixed layers of logs, snow and brushwood. You can burn an open fire in all types of brushwood shelter except the tree pit; in this case the walls are inclined to melt back and the bivi collapse.

The single lean-to shelter

The only problem with these shelters is that you must have a knife, saw or axe. The Eskimos have shown that with a knife you survive: without one you need a miracle.

When building this lean-to, make sure it is tactically located so that you can build a fire large enough to spread the warmth equally throughout the shelter. The shelter is improved by using a reflector of green logs with the fire.

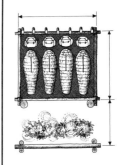

With the reflector correctly placed, the warm air from the fire should circulate as shown. The sleeping shelf insulated from the ground is vital as without it you will rapidly lose body heat to the ground.

The double lean-to shelter (right)

A larger group will be able to produce the more ambitious double lean-to, which is a lot warmer than the single lean-to.

The tree-pit shelter

This is a good option in an evasion environment when the only people looking for you are the enemy. The only drawback is that a fire tends to melt the walls and cause a collapse.

Teepee shelters (above and right)

This is a tent construction which can be easily built using a parachute (parateepee). It is possible to cook, eat, sleep and make signals from inside. You need a number of good poles about 3 to 4 metres long, or you can improvise as shown.

Elements for survival

The secret of successful travel in the Arctic is adequate clothing, sufficient food, rest, and a steady pace. You must have your kit: unless properly equipped, the best course of action is to 'hole up' and hope that the friendlies find you before the enemy does.

Arctic rations

However tired you are, you *must* eat all your rations. In the Arctic you burn enormous amounts of energy, and your rations are geared to replace this loss fully. It's all freeze-dried for convenience and lightness, and you melt snow to add to it.

Meat/rice rations must be simmered for about 20 minutes to make sure they have completely absorbed the moisture – otherwise, when eaten, they may cause stomach pains and will certainly contribute towards dehydration. The diet in the ration pack is balanced and is very nutritious, with plenty of 'brews' in the form of tea, coffee and beef stock. Again, you must drink well, and one of the cook's main jobs will be to see that plenty of hot water is available to top up Thermos flasks.

You have four types of pack to choose from. Breakfast is always porridge and hot chocolate. The main meal is usually eaten in the evening, and you carry the snack pack in your windproof for eating throughout the rest of the day. You may get a little fed up with the chocolate, but eat it; it contributes as much as anything else to your diet and wellbeing. One little

Arctic tent group stores

This is the usual cooking and lighting equipment for an eight-man tent group. The kit is set up and used by the cook but is distributed throughout the group to spread the weight. Ideally it will be carried on a pulk, as the tent group can survive without it.

1 Paraffin fuel containers
2 Funnel
3 Paraffin lamp
4 Lamp carrying case
5 Saucepans for melting snow and ice and for cooking
6 Pressure cooker
7 Peak fuel cooker
8 Issue fuel cooker and stove
9 Saucepan and frying pan handles
10 Frying pans
11 Pressure cooker inserts
12 Snow melting tins
13 Meta fuel blocks (for lamps)

tip is to carry some curry powder with you to add to any food you're getting bored with.

Lamps and cookers

There are various types, but they work on the same principle. All burn deleaded petrol (naptha), which is the only fuel that should be used, except in emergency. Leaded fuel causes poisoning and 'tenteye'. Even with naptha you need some ventilation.

Your cookers are vital equipment. Constantly check them – nuts, bolts

Water

Thirst is a major problem in the arctic: in order to conserve fuel for other purposes the survivor often deprives himself of drinking water from melting ice and snow, and the time and energy required to chop and collect ice for water also limits the supply. You may become dangerously dehydrated in the Arctic as easily as in a desert.

Remember:
1 You need about 50 per cent more fuel to produce the same quantity of water from snow than from melting ice.

2 It is safe, within limits, to eat snow as long as you allow the snow to thaw sufficiently to be moulded into a stick or ball.
3 Do not eat snow in its natural state; it will cause dehydration and chill your body.
4 Do not eat crushed ice as it may cause injury to your lips and tongue.
5 Any surface that absorbs the sun's heat can be used to melt ice or snow, e.g. a flat rock, a dark tarpaulin or a signal panel.
6 The milky water of glacial streams can be drunk once the sediment has been allowed to settle out.

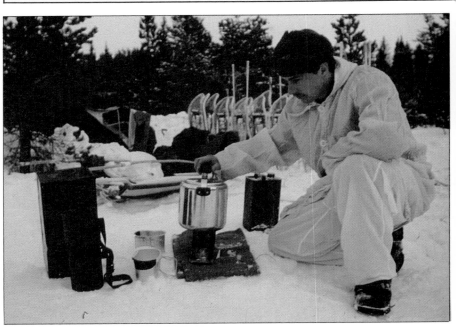

Left: Lighting the paraffin lamps is best not done in the dark. The basic drill is to fill the lamp with fuel, pump up the pressure, preheat the vapouriser with meta blocks, and then switch the fuel on.

Above: Pressure-cooking food greatly reduces the amount of fuel you need, and the cooking time.

Making a fire in the Arctic

You have waterproof matches in your kit.

1 Dig down to the frozen earth for your firebase. If this is not possible, build a base of logs over the snow. You need a layer of brushwood, a layer of snow, then another layer of each, finally topped off with good thick layers of logs.
2 Build your fire on this base.
3 Use tinder to start the fire. If tinder is a problem, you can always find dry spruce twigs in the lowest branches, peel off birch bark, or use fir root. All contain high concentrations of tar and burn with a long-lasting flame. Fir root is especially good.
6 If you need to use fuel to help the fire along, dip your twigs in it and soak them. Don't waste fuel by pouring it on.
7 Use dead tree logs as the main fuel. It burns best.

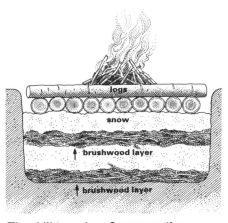

The skill to make a fire means the difference between death and survival. Alaskan air crew suffer their winter survival course in a rather more demanding environment than British air crew.

and gaskets tend to come loose – and carry spare parts in your pulk.

Light and fill cookers and lamps in the open – particularly in training. On operations, you may have to risk lighting them inside your shelter. Make sure the filler cap is properly screwed on, and use the filler funnel to avoid waste. Remember, the naptha must live in its pit outside your tent.

Most lamps and cookers need preheating to generate a gas pressure build-up before you can light them. Use 'meta' (methylated spirit impregnated) blocks to do this – never use naptha.

Rules for health

When you're living in the Arctic:

1 Keep fit

You burn enormous amounts of energy just doing simple jobs. The fitter you are, the less energy you burn, and you can work without becoming exhausted. This reduces the danger of freezing.

2 Drink plenty of water

Dehydration causes tiredness. Drink even if you're not thirsty. Do not eat unmelted snow: it chills your body and can give cramps.

3 Eat your rations

Even if you're not hungry, keep eating. Regular, hot food will keep you at your peak.

4 Maintain a positive attitude

Keep alert and, above all, cheerful. You can make it!

Right and below: A field kitchen equipped with the large pressurized petrol stove caters for company-sized groups and above. This is heavy kit, usually moved by a vehicle.

The Arctic paraffin lamp

1 Fill the tank and screw down the cap firmly.
2 Check that the mantle is undamaged.
3 Lift the glass by slackening the ventilator nut and place four lighted meta blocks around the bottom.
4 Pump up the pressure vigorously while the meta blocks burn.
5 Switch the fuel on and if you have sufficient pressure the fuel will vapourise and the mantle will glow. If not, you will end up with a small fire in the glass. If this happens, switch off the fuel and start again.

ventilator nut
ventilator
handle
mantle (very delicate: be careful not to damage it)
Pyrex globe
gas tip cleaning lever
fuel valve
filler cap
pump
tank

Protection from the cold
Tents and Tentsheets

To carry on fighting effectively you need warmth and food, and in the Arctic this means, first of all, protection from the weather. You must learn how to live in the snow: how to use tents, tentsheets, cookers and lamps, and how to keep yourself fit and healthy.

Tents and tentsheets

Tents can sleep five or 10 men and are large and bulky; they tend to be used in base areas, and generally have to be carried on a vehicle or on a 'pulk' – a man-towable sledge. The tents used by British forces are the Canadian single-pole or British ridge tent.

If you are working in small groups, you will not be able to carry a tent, so you will each carry a tentsheet. In its simplest form this is a diamond of canvas, with buttons and buttonholes on each edge. They can be joined together to form a tent of almost any size, but normally it would be for eight to 10 men: the tentgroup.

Tentsheets give you a portable,

The two-man tentgroup

The tent sheet is the basic unit from which you can make a simple two-man tent, using two sheets.

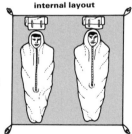

ski stick in centre

pegs

internal layout

Kit layout is all-important. These tents are extremely cramped and you must decide where everything is stored so that you can move out at speed and your oppo can pack your kit when you are not there.

The four-man tentgroup

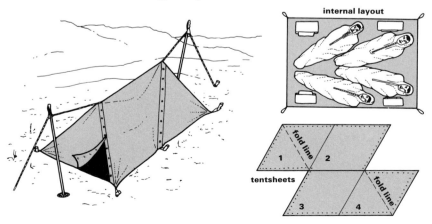

internal layout

tentsheets

The ways in which the tent sheet is folded and joined to produce different-size tents is not obvious, and must be thoroughly practised in dry training before you get out on the ground. Each man in the section must have an exact 'job description' so that the tent is erected as a drill.

windproof, lightproof, robust a[nd] flexible system that meets all t[he] needs of survival and tactics. It tak[es] time to construct a shelter using te[nt] sheets, and you will need to be able [to] do it quickly when the temperature [is] 20° below freezing, so practise no[w]. And learn to live in it.

Siting and pitching your te[nt]

The tentgroup commander w[ill] direct this very simple drill for pitc[h]ing a tent.

1 Select the best site
Look for shelter from wind and t[he] enemy, and make sure the snow [is] deep enough to dig your shelter in.

2 Stow your kit
This should be neatly stowed to o[ne] side, normally to the left of the [in]tended doorway.

3 Level the site
Level to near ground level. The te[nt] group commander will designate t[he] area to dig.

4 Find insulation
At the same time, designated men fi[nd] brushwood and undergrowth to use [as] insulation.

Duties of the c[ook]

Follow these drills and responsibilities and [it] will ease congestion in your tent or tentshe[et] when you first pitch it. A familiar routine w[ill] also keep your spirits up! The cook should:

1 Be the first man in – with his cooker and lamp – and may raise the pole.
2 Arrange the sleeping mats and bags as t[hey] are passed in to him.
3 Arrange the collection of rations and clea[n] snow.
4 Cook the rations and, with the help of ot[her] members of the tent group, arrange:
  • The filling of stoves and lamps. Initially [?] stoves should be used; snow takes a lo[ng] time to melt.

The five-man tentgroup

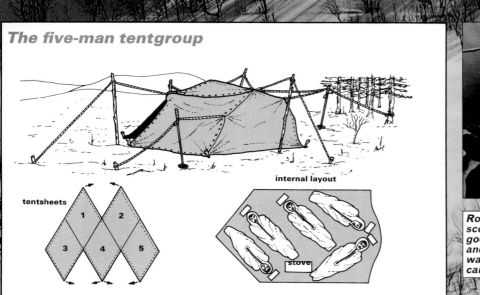

tentsheets

1	2
3	4 5

internal layout

stove

This is the usual half-section or fireteam layout, complete with stove. Ideally you should not use ski poles in the construction of the tent as you may need them in a hurry.

Royal Marine Commandos get into some scoff. Once you are inside the tent it is a good idea to take your outer layers off and carefully brush off all the snow: that way your kit will not get wet. If it does, it can freeze solid when you move outside.

Below: The members of this ski march in northern Norway are carrying over 30 kg of equipment each. This is the only way to move over much of Allied Forces North command: there is a single-track railway from Oslo, but this only reaches as far as Bodö. The main north/south road needs constant snow clearance in winter.

The seven-man tentgroup

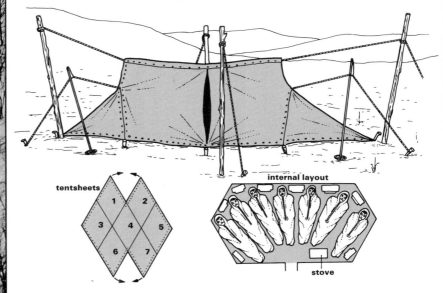

tentsheets

1	2
3	4 5
6	7

internal layout

stove

● The collection of more clean snow and ice for melting.
● The collection of rubbish.
● A constant supply of hot water. Empty flasks are used for storage.
Organise a hot drink if flasks are empty.
Use his imagination to make the ration as satisfying as possible: for example, curry powder, onions and bacon all add flavour.
Have the next meal prepared, as far as possible: this saves time and effort later.

Remember, the health and morale of your group hinges on your expertise and hard work as the cook.

Everyone's feet face the door and the cook sleeps next to the stove. If you are operating a sentry stag, make sure the stag list is written so that the sentry wakes up the person who sleeps next to him, which means sentries do not have to trample over people looking for the next man on the stag list.

This is not difficult, but you must get it down to a fine art: you'll get cold if you find yourself standing around. Work out how long it takes you: this is your 'pull pole' time. It should be around 15 minutes when properly practised. This will help you make plans to go straight from the tent to work that keeps you warm.

Brush off ice and snow before packing away, or you will be carrying unnecessary weight and it will take you longer to put the shelter up again.

Weapon pits or trenches

Naptha snow b...

The tentgroup commander's duties

As commander, it is your responsibility to plan and organise the following:

1 Correct pitching of the tent or tentsheets
2 Allocation of sleeping space
3 Storage of weapons and equipment
4 Sentry roster and alert states
5 Routine for drying clothes
6 Fire precautions
7 Blackout drills
8 Track and camouflage discipline
9 De-icing of tent
10 Foot inspections
11 Overall welfare of your men

A paratrooper camouflages the issue ridge tent from the air with a white flysheet. The snow walls around the tent provide cover as well as protection from the elements. The fighting position on the right has been camouflaged with a few branches to minimise the shadow of the trench from the air.

Once the tent is up, your immediate priority is camouflage. Issue white camouflage netting gives good cover, but you must use poles to avoid shadows formed by the shape of the tent.

Tentgroup stores

The commander must make sure that the following are carried, and that they work.

1 Pulk
2 Tent (5- or 10-man)
3 Snowshoes (if not being worn)
4 Snow shovels (2)
5 Stove and spares (2)
6 Pressure cooker
7 Lantern with case plus spares, including mantlets (1 or 2)
8 Machete (gollock) and case
9 Saucepan
10 Fuel funnel
11 Fuel containers: 2-gal, 1-gal or ½-gal
12 Ski/pulk repair kit

Alternatives are:
1 Tentsheets (1 per man)
2 Fuel containers, 1 or 2 pint (5)
3 Two-man stoves (1 per 2 men)

Note: The amount of fuel carried will depend on the time to be spent in the field.

5 Install cooking kit
The designated cook unpacks the cooking kit, lights the stove and gets the rations ready for cooking. The lamp is lit.

6 Lay the tent
The tent is laid out with the door positioned away from the enemy (and, ideally, away from the prevailing wind) so that they will not be able to see any light.

7 Raise the tent
Peg the edges down and raise the tent on its own poles, if you have them; otherwise use brushwood poles. Do not use your skis or sticks except in an emergency. The cook takes the lamp, cooker, rations etc into the tent.

8 Settle in
Weatherproof the edges of the tent with snow (thrown over brushwood, which prevents icing and allows easy dismantling). The cook begins to heat the water (use clean, fresh snow, stored in plastic bags). Pass in sleeping mats and bags and lay them out. Make sure that the floor is flat; otherwise everyone will slide during the night and lose sleep, and the snow will harden into uncomfortable lumps. Dig a cold hole by the door.

9 Food and warmth
By now it will be pretty warm from the stove and lamp. Two men will finish off the outside ski pit, weapons rack, fuel pit and latrine but everyone else is thinking about food and admin, such as weapon and equipment maintenance. When you have eaten, night routine will begin.

It's −20°C outside, but you got your drills right and so you kept warm while the shelter was erected. Now you're inside you're comfortable in your shirtsleeves! It only took 15 minutes – and that's as good as a fully trained Arctic soldier.

Layout of the eight-man tentgroup

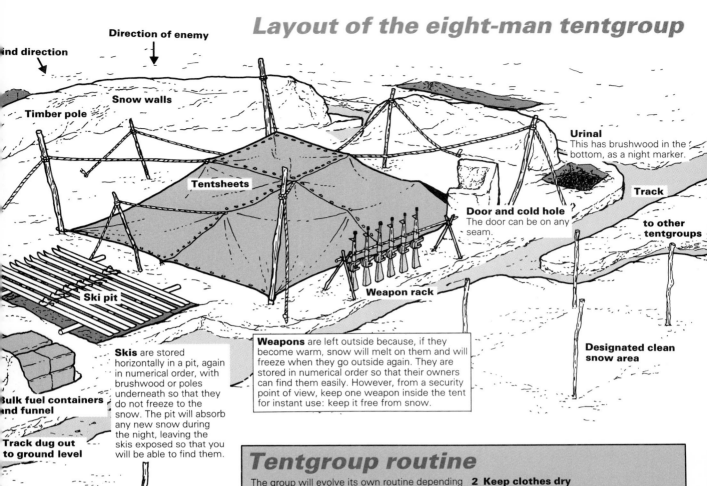

Wind direction

Direction of enemy

Snow walls

Timber pole

Tentsheets

Ski pit

Urinal
This has brushwood in the bottom, as a night marker.

Track

Door and cold hole
The door can be on any seam.

to other tentgroups

Weapon rack

Designated clean snow area

Skis are stored horizontally in a pit, again in numerical order, with brushwood or poles underneath so that they do not freeze to the snow. The pit will absorb any new snow during the night, leaving the skis exposed so that you will be able to find them.

Bulk fuel containers and funnel

Track dug out to ground level

Latrine is marked with brushwood and pole to make sure it can be found after a snowstorm.

Weapons are left outside because, if they become warm, snow will melt on them and will freeze when they go outside again. They are stored in numerical order so that their owners can find them easily. However, from a security point of view, keep one weapon inside the tent for instant use: keep it free from snow.

Tentgroup routine

The group will evolve its own routine depending on tactical conditions, but the commander and cook always sleep by the door. Cooking is also done by the door (in case of fire and to allow moisture to escape) or in the cold hole. Other points for comfortable tent life are:

1 Control your kit
You will be cramped, so keep your kit packed unless you need it. Don't lose your gloves or hat.

2 Keep clothes dry
Dry damp clothing by hanging it in the ceiling of the tent. When the heat is off, take it into your sleeping bag; this includes your boots.

3 Check your feet
You and your buddy should help each other to do this. Powder them and put on dry socks. If your feet are cold, rub them or, even better, warm them in your buddy's armpits! If they are seriously cold, don't rub them; just use the armpit method.

The Jelper Sledge

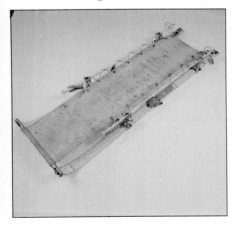

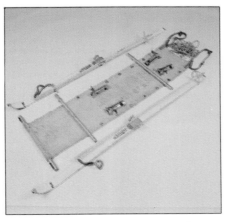

The Jelper Sledge is the equivalent of the stretcher. It is the Arctic method of casualty evacuation, although it is also used for carrying light loads.

The central sheet has an idiot's guide on how to make up the sledge from ordinary skis and ski poles and the kit. It is designed to use one man's ski kit in its construction, for obvious reasons.

GPMG pulk

A specialist pulk is available for the GPMG in the sustained-fire role and enables the weapon and the huge quantities of ammunition it requires to be pulled into position and deployed at speed. You can fire off the pulk.

1493

Finding Emergency Food in the Arctic

There is little to eat in the Arctic in winter, but in an emergency there are some possibilities. Look out for bird and animal tracks; these may lead you to their sources of food, which will probably be safe to eat.

But beware: if you find berries or something you don't recognise, they may be poisonous. Try a small quantity, on your tongue first of all, and if there are no ill effects eat a little; wait up to eight hours and then eat a bit more. If after another eight hours you are all right, you can be reasonably sure that the food is safe. Be especially wary of fungi: don't touch them in training unless one of you is a real expert.

For safety, then, you are limited to animals, birds and fish.

Animals

Arctic animals range from reindeer, moose and bear (brown and polar) to hares, rabbits, squirrels and lemmings (look under rocks for these). You will also come across wolves and foxes.

Look at the snow in the mornings and you will realise from the number of tracks just how much wildlife there is. The closer to the treeline or shoreline you are, the more abundant wildlife becomes, even in winter.

Hunting animals is a skill, but you will soon master it if your life depends on it. Points to remember are:

1 Always hunt up-wind (with the wind in your face).
2 Move slowly.
3 Try to stalk from above.
4 Crawl if you are on exposed ground; move while the animal is feeding, and freeze when it lifts its head up.
5 Don't take too long a shot, and if using issue ammo (which has solid heads) shoot through the heart, although small ground game may have to be shot through the head.
6 A sharp whistle will cause most animals to stop: time enough to give you the chance of a shot.

Birds

The most common Arctic bird is the ptarmigan or snow grouse, which is

The 24-hour Arctic ration pack

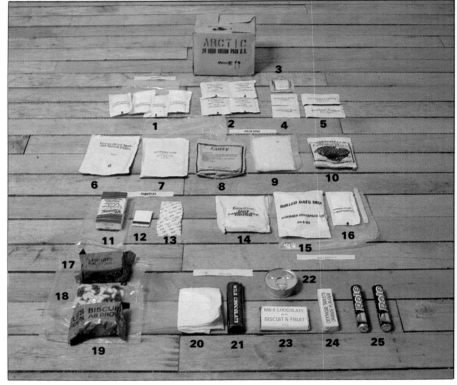

1 Sugar packets	**13** Salt	
2 Powdered milk	**14** Chocolate drink	
3 Beef stock drink	**15** Rolled oats mix	
4 Instant tea	**16** Sugar	
5 Instant coffee	**17** Biscuits fruit AB	
6 Instant dried apple and apricot flakes	**18** Nuts and raisins	
7 Vegetable soup	**19** Biscuits brown AB	
8 Dehydrated beef curry	**20** Toilet paper	
9 Rice	**21** Milk chocolate	
10 Dried peas	**22** Beef spread	
11 Tissues	**23** Chocolate and biscuit bar	
12 Matches	**24** Dextrose tablets	
	25 Chocolate covered caramels	

Spare arctic ration packs are carried by each man as part of his survival kit. These rations will buy you the time to find help or find or catch food.

You may find yourself in need of survival rations closer to home than the Arctic. The UK weather can certainly provide a challenge for RAF Mountain Rescue teams.

Trapping

Fall log trap for big game

rock weight · parachute buckle · bail · stockade

Spring and spear trap

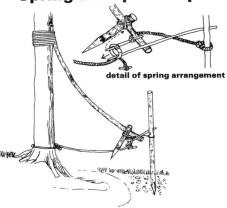

detail of spring arrangement

Trip deadfall

deadfall · fixed end · balance point · tripwire · free end · pivot

Large and medium sized game is usually caught in deadfalls. However, this method is only worthwhile if there are sufficient quantities of larger game available.

The spear trap is another method of catching larger mammals but requires very careful construction to be effective.

A rock deadfall of this type stretched across an animal trail is effective as long as you are able to canalise the animal into the trap.

relatively tame and can be killed with a stick or stone in a trap. There are owls and ravens too, but both are wily and you will need a baited trap. Near the coast, you will find gulls; these can be killed with a gorge hook. To trap birds you need some sort of cage system, to be triggered as the bird takes the bait or by you from a hidden position.

Seals and walruses

These are found along the coastline or, on a good day, lying next to their breathing holes out on the ice. Both have large amounts of blubber, which is useful for cooking, heating and lighting, and is also edible, along with the flesh. You need to take great care when stalking a seal, and ideally you should shoot it through the head; this

will make sure it cannot reach its breathing hole, and it will float if it's in water.

Harpoons and spears

You can make these from a piece of stout timber, their tips hardened in a fire, or with a knife or suitably-shaped stone or bone bound onto one end. They are best used to finish off an animal that has already been caught in a trap.

Snares

If you do not have any customised snares, you can use string or light wire. The secret of success is to make sure that the slide moves smoothly: you can improvise with bone or a button, or a spring-loaded system. Once it is set, run a flame round the snare, to reduce human smell. Set the snare on a natural game trail, preferably in a narrow place or gap. Use bait if you can.

Fish

There is an abundance of fish in the Arctic, not only in the sea but also

Harpoons and fish spears

If you are near shallow water (waist deep) where fish are large and plentiful, you may be able to spear them. Try to find a straight sapling with a solid core that you can sharpen to a point. If not, tie a bayonet or pointed piece of metal or sharp bone to the end. Next, find a rock or bank which overlooks a fish run and wait for the fish to swim past.

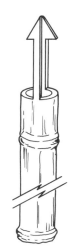

bamboo   metal   metal   bone

under the ice of frozen lakes, generally towards the inflow or outflow. You will have to cut holes in the ice for your lines. Make hooks from safety pins, tin openers, bones etc; bait can be inedible parts such as the entrails of animals or fish. The best fishing method is to put out night lines, which you check each morning, but where the bait needs to be moved

about you must make 'jigs' using discarded food tins, silver paper or other shiny material. Cod will take your clasp knife!

For weights, use stones; for floats, a piece of wood. Animal tendons make very strong traces which are almost invisible and are ideal for attaching hooks to lines.

The Arctic is harsh, but you can still

RAF aircrew fish through the ice. Note the axe and drill needed to cut the hole. The clothing they are wearing, known as 'Extreme foul weather', is issued for operations in Canada and Norway.

live off the land as long as you have one or two basic items with you. Go for what seems to be plentiful; don't waste time or energy; and above all be patient and determined.

The automatic fisherman

Fish can be caught in winter, through a hole in the ice. Once you have cut it you can stop it freezing over by covering it with brush and heaping snow over the top. Fish tend to gather in deep pools, so if you are lake fishing cut your hole over the deepest part.

You will need several holes which you can fish simultaneously using the 'automatic fisherman'. The fish pulls the flag upright. You need a one-metre pole and enough line to reach well beyond the ice. Attach a spoon-shaped spinner from a ration pack can to the line, and place the hook slightly below it.

Improvised fish hooks

Wood skewer
Buried in the bait, this hook sticks in the side of the fish's mouth

Thorn
An awkward piece of thorn can be effective when buried in the bait.

Thorn
A thorn bush with large rearward pointing barbs is ideal

Bone
A sharp piece of bone can be fixed to a suitable piece of wood.

Nails
Ordinary nails can be bent into shape or set into wood.

Preparing fish

Bleeding
As soon as you catch a fish, cut out the gills and large blood vessels next to the backbone.

Sealing
Remove the scales by scraping with a knife.

Gutting
Gut the fish by cutting it open and scraping out the guts.

Skinning
Some fish, such as catfish, have no scales and can be skinned.

1497

Overseas Intervention

French special forces units began as Free French units fighting with the **SAS** during World War II.

The French Marine base at Lorient was quiet, for on sundays only the working staff are present. In the command centre a signals operator checks the telex as it types out its message. The Commandos have been put on to full alert! The duty officer alerts all units immediately. Some men were recalled from leave, while others prepared equipment at their bases for rapid deployment. It was a well tried-and-tested system. Maintained at a high state of readiness, the Commando groups were each airlifted by French airforce Transalls to Hyères where helicopters would ferry them to the waiting assault ships.

Although in this case it was only an exercise, French Commando forces have been in action frequently over the last 30 years, fighting in Algeria, Tchad, Beirut and French islands in the Pacific.

In this recent exercise, the Com-

Above: In Indochina and the war in Algeria, French forces relied on the MAT-49 sub-machine gun, a robust and straightforward weapon which remains in service alongside the 5.56-mm FA MAS assault rifle.

Right: A paradrop in NBC kit is a bizarre sight, but just part of the training programme for troops assigned to France's Rapid Deployment Force. Over 47,000 troops stand ready to fight overseas on a word from the Élysée.

mandos were required to infiltrate an island group designated the "Independent Islands", which had been invaded by hostile forces. Their role was to recce the main island and designate landing beaches, identifying them with markers, and locate suitable landing zones for helicopters to pave the way for a swift and successful landing by the amphibious troops of the Marine Infantry Division and French Foreign Legion.

French submarine

Lying about 100 nautical miles from the Independent Islands, a French submarine waited at periscope depth. On board were 10 Commando combat swimmers from the *Hubert* group: the French equivalent of the British Special Boat Squadron. Heading for an RV with the submarine was a Transall with a further 14 men of the group aboard. Six men parachuted into the sea and entered the submarine while it remained submerged; the remainder joined the task force to provide a combat swimmer detachment at Commando headquarters.

With the men aboard, the submarine continued its unseen journey, moving close to the main island and allowing the swimmers to swim ashore and undertake the vital reconnaissance missions.

Intelligence reports from the combat swimmers were transmitted to Commando HQ, who in turn passed them on to the task force commander's HQ, who formulated the overall plans of pre-assault, assault and post-assault security. The Commando group commanders were briefed on their roles in the forthcoming operation.

Raiding craft attack

The *Hubert* group will go ashore first, using their Zodiac raiding craft, capable of speeds up to 30 knots. Their objective is to capture and put out of action a radar station sited on the western side of the island. Once that is achieved they will move towards the enemy to create a diversion, giving the impression that the attack is coming from the west. For this they will have to carry heavy weapons and large quantities of ammunition. *Jambet, Trepel, de Penfentenys* and *de Montfort* groups will move ashore to pre-empt the actual landing. *Jambet*'s mission is to capture and hold the island's eastern beach, following the markers placed by the combat swimmers. Once the beach is secured, they will move to pre-designated helicopter landing

zones and cover the arrival of the Super Frelon helicopters carrying the *de Montfort* group. Also with this group will be the Liaison Observation Detachment, who will direct naval gunfire support and air strikes, and the officer in charge of the landings, whose job it is to ensure that everybody lands ashore in the right place. The *Trepel* group's mission is to capture the radio station in the northern

French commandos are trained to arrive by all means, including HALO parachuting or by submarine. They train for all conditions, from the Jura in winter to exercises in the Indian Ocean from the French base at Djibouti.

A Naval Super Frelon unloads at a 'captured' airfield during an exercise. The personnel are a mixture of conscripts doing their national service and career soldiers.

Fighting Fit

A Transall C-160 brings in more French troops to N'Djamena airport during the French intervention in Chad during 1986. French commandos were deployed there in response to the Libyan-backed invasion, which was thoroughly defeated.

Above: Test your bottle with the AMX-13 nerve test! This potentially terminal exercise in courage certainly persuades you to get your timing right. The commando groups have a much higher proportion of regular soldiers to conscripts than other French forces.

sector of the island's capital and then to mark out and defend the helicopter landing zones, where the Marine Infantry will land from Puma helicopters. In the north of the island, a small port is the target for the *de Penfentenys* group, who are tasked with disabling enemy naval craft, preventing them putting to sea and counterattacking. *De Montfort*'s group provides a detachment to support the *Jambet* group while the rest of the unit stays in reserve under the control of Commando HQ.

This scenario is typical of the type of operation undertaken by the French Marine Commandos, who have to operate from surface vessels, submarines and both fixed-wing and rotary aircraft. They are an élite force, well trained and able to operate in all environments. They were formed originally during World War II as part of Allied commando forces.

SAS origins

Britain's forces had developed highly mobile units that could go ashore and strike at the enemy, destroying defences and local command centres. Every man was a volunteer and underwent gruelling training. Those who passed through this course wore the coveted 'green beret' of newly formed Commando troops. In 1944 Britain allowed foreign troops to train for commando operations. Lieutenant Commander Keiffer was chosen to assemble the first Free

French volunteers, and it was a year later that he assumed command of the 1st Battalion of French commando fusiliers. Those first French commandos took part in numerous raids on the European coast, and took their rightful place as the first troops ashore at Ouistreham (Westerham) on 6 June 1944. The battalion was disbanded after the war, but during 1946-47 the French government decided to reestablish a commando force for rapid

deployment in its overseas territories. As in Britain, the commando role was given to the Marines and six independent commando units, and were formed under names of commando officers killed in action during the war.

The present-day French Marine Commandos comprise five combat commando groups since the *Francois* commando was disbanded in 1952. In an operational role they are under command of the Major-in-Chief of the Marines, while their equipment and its maintenance come under the Marine Fusiliers Command (COFUSMA), which is comprised of the Marine Commando groups, the Security Companies and the Marine School at Lorient.

For the past 15 years Lorient has been the home base for the Commandos and will remain so, for modernisation of the facilities ensures continuation. The only unit not permanently based there is the *Hubert* group of combat swimmers.

Below: Combat swimmers of the **Hubert** group are the equivalent of the British **SBS** and specialise in recce work ahead of amphibious landings and raids on enemy shipping and shore installations.

Combat Report

Palestine:
Anti-Terrorist Patrol in Jerusalem

The commander of a Scottish Rifle Company describes an incident which interrupted the Saint Andrew's Day celebrations.

The Officers of 1st Battalion, The Argyll and Sutherland Highlanders looked splendid in their tropical Mess dress, comprising kilt, dress sporran, white jacket, bow tie and miniature medals. The ancient walls of our Mess in the Hospice Notre Dame de France, a lovely old building in Jerusalem near the Old City, added to the scene. In the Mess dining room regimental silver gleamed on the table and, somewhere in the further rooms, pipers could be faintly heard tuning their instruments. It was Saint Andrew's Day, a day which is more or less ignored by Scots when in their own country, but which is celebrated with almost religious fervour by Scots abroad. This night was going to be a pleasant change from a cold night on patrol, or at a road block, with the promise of a good meal and an excellent party.

The first salvo of mortar bombs shook the windows, and rattled the glasses and then the sound of heavy small arms fire was clearly heard not very far away. The Colonel calmly put down his glass and said "Road Block Company, you know your duties; off you go. Other Companies, I will give orders in a few minutes when we know what is happening!"

This was on 30 November 1946 in Jerusalem, Palestine. Field Marshal Montgomery, who at that time was Chief of the Imperial General Staff, was visiting the country then, and the terrorist activity that night was obviously connected with the Field Marshal's presence. It was a show of force more than anything, I think. What happened was that a force of Jewish terrorists had quietly occupied flats overlooking the Mustapha Police Station, and on a given signal had opened fire on the station with mortars, small arms, grenades and home-made explosive devices. Being always ready for something of this nature, the Palestine Police reacted quickly and a good old fire fight commenced.

Violent disturbances

By a minor drain of Officers on courses, postings and leave at that period I found myself, a Lieutenant at the tender age of twenty-one commanding a Rifle Company. Now it appeared I was going to lead it into action!

The Colonel speedily told us the situation as he knew it, which at that stage was very confused. Our orders were basically to take our men to Mustapha Police Station and sort the situation out. We hurried to the place where our soldiers were waiting, beside our transport, and I gave my Platoon Commanders a quick briefing, which they passed down the line. As we did this, the explosions from the direction of the attacked Police Station became louder, and the small arms fire crackled on the night air with the strange echoing effect that it has amongst high buildings. Very quickly we were on the move. Each vehicle had a Bren gun lined over the cab, and every soldier pointed his rifle or Sten gun outwards, ready for a possible ambush.

We debussed about a quarter of a mile from the Police Station, and the din of battle was deafening. One Company was sent to storm the flats where the attackers were firing from, while my Company (to my disappointment) were detailed to form a cordon and stop line to cut off any escaping terrorists. I should mention here that our road blocks, referred to earlier, were already in position. They were a standard

A British armoured car blocks the road to catch terrorists fleeing from the scene of their latest outrage.

procedure whenever any terrorist incident took place, and had already proved their worth. They had code names of fish – 'Roach' 'Perch' and so forth. Without any orders, in the event of say, a bomb exploding, standby troops would dash out, and place these blocks at strategic roads in the centre of Jerusalem. Three times they had caught terrorists hurrying by vehicles away from the scene of their misdeeds.

My Company that night was to be a kind of extension to these road blocks, but on the edge of the battle itself. As I moved my men into position bullets continued to crack overhead, with the odd one striking high up on buildings nearby. I recall thinking at the time that an awful lot of ammunition was being wasted! In the darkened streets which went in all directions, map reading was not easy, and I found that two of my sections were in the wrong place. I managed to resolve the situation speedily by saying that as many soldiers as possible were to get on, and into the American Jeep. The first lift took thirteen of us, which showed what a versatile little vehicle that was!

Very soon after that our other Company attacked the terrorists in the flats, and things ended quickly. The opposition did not stay to tangle with tough professionals, and all they left behind in the wrecked rooms were bloodstains, a number of live rounds and grenades and a lot of empty cases. What casualties they suffered

were never precisely known, though British newspapers giving details of the action gave all sorts of high figures. We had no casualties and the Police only several wounded. However, the damage to buildings and property was extensive. My men and I then carried out a careful search of the general area in case of hiding terrorists, but found no one. Then we packed up and went back to our vehicles and barracks.

I suddenly realised that I was very tired and very thirsty. Why is one always thirsty in action?) My Jocks offloaded their kit, and unloaded and checked their weapons. Their morale was high, though they were disappointed at not having had the chance of actually shooting at anything. Referring to the visit of the Field Marshal, I heard one soldier say "Well, Monty would feel at home anyway!"

I joined my soldiers for a cup of tea from their operational 'haybox' containers. As I stood there sipping it, and listening to the quiet chat going on around me, I reflected on the fact that the Officers' Mess was now closed and silent, and thought of the excellent Saint Andrew's Night dinner and party that we should have had. Wasn't it General Sherman who said "War is hell!"

A patrol from the Argyll and Sutherland Highlanders heads down a street in the Manshiya quarter of Jerusalem at the height of the terrorist campaign.

From Lorient to Djibouti

Like the SA 80, the FA MAS assault rifle is a bullpup 5.56-mm weapon, which makes it much more convenient for commando operations than the MAS 49/56 rifle it has only recently replaced. French Marines practise cliff assault from the sea and regularly go to the Pyrenees for climbing and skiing. One commando group is always stationed at Djibouti as part of France's Indian Ocean force.

All French Marine commandos wear the green beret and a badge that has been handed down from the first French commandos, who saw action in World War II. It comprises a brig, a dagger and the Cross of Lorraine (the symbol of Free France), all set onto a shield. The 'green beret' is awarded after undertaking the gruelling commando course, for which every man is a volunteer. Apart from the commando qualification, every man is parachute-trained to a basic standard. Specialisation as parachute instructors, combat shooting instructors, and for combat swimming, mountain warfare, signals, demolitions and explosives, high altitude parachuting and sniper marksmanship are undertaken to develop the individual commando's skill and the operational capability of the commando groups.

As commandos they have at their disposal a wide range of weapons and specialist equipment, including state-of-the-art optical and laser sights and high-burst transmission radio sets. Because of their rapid response role the heaviest weapons in their armoury are the 12.7-mm machine-guns, 81-mm mortars and MILAN anti-tank missiles.

Amphibious raiding

Although they regularly use parachutes and helicopters as a method of infiltration, amphibious raiding is still a prime role. The principal craft used by the commandos and combat swimmers is the Zodiac Mk III raiding boat, powered by a 40-hp outboard engine,

No time to admire the scenery during climbing practice in the south of France. On exercises, the commandos are often tasked with raiding important French defence installations, which sharpens their skill and improves key point security.

and the PB IV, which is a semi-rigid boat using two 40-hp outboard engines. Each commando group has 14 Zodiacs and two PB IVs in its inventory, and the combat swimmers also have canoes and swimmer delivery vehicles for their specialised role.

Commandos can expect to spend between 200 and 250 days a year away from base on exercises, operations and specialist training courses. They are committed to strike raids or reconnaissance missions either independently or as part of a large amphibious or land-based operation. Their training brings them into close contact with the Marine Infantry, of which they are not part, as well as conventional land-based army units.

Underwater attacks

Within the scope of training, they will undertake simulated underwater attacks against ships of the navy and attempt to breach the security defences of strategic bases to test their attack abilities and seek out weaknesses in the defences. Normally seen moving at speed in their fast raiding craft and disembarking in rocky inlets, they can be found ski-ing in the Pyrenees or undertaking high-altitude parachute descents into the African bush.

Apart from the continuous programme of training and exercises, one commando group is always based at Djibouti as part of France's maritime rapid deployment force in the Indian Ocean. The commandos regularly train in different climates and terrains, and must be able to rapidly adapt to new surroundings. This can mean operating without vehicles or support craft, and in conjunction with local armed forces of foreign countries.

The 'Cocoys'

Within the French Marines, the Commandos, are the élite. They are equally at home in their blue dress ceremonial uniform, the camouflaged combat fatigues of the African desert, or the waterproof over-suit used with their rubber inflatable boats. They are the 'Cocoys', as the familiar nickname of the commandos titles them, along with their motto, "United We Conquer".

In addition to the Marine Commandos, the French navy has a larger formation, the *Marine Fusiliers*. Like the Royal Marines, they provide detachments of troops to serve aboard warships, and security companies to protect naval installations ashore. They

*Above: Mobile **MILAN** anti-tank missile posts are used throughout the French rapid deployment force and are the heaviest weapons used by the French Marines, whose mobile role rules out anything heavier.*

Below: For amphibious raiding the French Marines employ everything from small dinghies to the powered Zodiac assault craft and semi-rigid boats. The commandos are the elite of the French Marines and will spearhead any French amphibious intervention.

Fighting Fit

number some 200 officers, 1,500 senior NCOs and 2,000 other ranks. An integral part of the navy, they use naval rank designations. All recruits, conscripts and officer cadets attend the Marine School at Lorient, alongside the base of the Marine Commandos and the amphibious centre, all under the aegis of the Marine Command (Cosfuma).

Assigned to units

Officers are trained to become commanders of Marine companies, capable of leading them in many specialised operations. The initial training lasts four months, after which time the new officer is assigned to a Marine unit. It is at this point that the officer can elect to volunteer for commando training and gain a diploma in parachuting.

The Marine enters for seven weeks' training to gain his elementary certificate, which centres on basic military requirements, physical training, firearms and combat instruction. At this point those selected for commando training separate from those who are to join a security company or a warship.

Security duties

Assigned to a security company, the Marine will find himself tasked with guarding and defending strategic bases, arsenals, dockyards and naval air stations as well as communication and command centres. A major priority for the security detachments

Above: River crossing while on exercise in France. Note the distinctive shape of the French helmet, which replaced the old US helmet during the 1960s.

Right: Parachute training is on offer even for the conscripts posted to the Marine security companies. The majority of the security detachments deployed around the nuclear weapons stores and other important facilities are national servicemen.

is the nuclear weapons stores.

Security Marines' work includes the guarding of underground bases, where they are armed with sub-machine-guns. Up to two-thirds of the Security units are made up of conscripts and promotion is dependent upon the individual. They too have the opportunity to undertake a basic parachuting course.

Marine Fusiliers serve aboard frigates and larger warships, and are tasked with their defence whilst at sea or alongside, plus amphibious operations in conjunction with Marines

from other vessels. After two years' service all Marines, including Commandos, can undertake training for the second level certificate course in technical competence (BAT). This is a senior NCO's course and lasts six months. This is also an inducement to conscripts who have enjoyed their service to volunteer for the regulars.

This sniper in Chad is armed with the French FR-F1 sniper rifle, a bolt action weapon chambered for the 7.5-mm×54 cartridge. One foot of the integral bipod can be seen projecting forward of the shooter's left hand.